Take a line for a swim.

Draw a self-portrait without lo
pencil off the paper. Sign your nar

This book belongs to

_____

Aquanauts

sidekickBOOKS

First published in 2017 by

SIDEKICK BOOKS
42 Silvester Road
London SE22 9PB

Printed by
The Russell Press

Typeset in Vollkorn and Gill Sans

~

ISBN: 978-1-909560-26-0

Cover art and design by Jon Stone

HOW TO USE THIS BOOK

Read it. Write in it. Take it with you.

Make it your own.

The exercises in *Aquanauts* are there for you to carry out or ignore as you will. If you want to fill up these pages differently – with cuttings, sketches, journal entries or otherwise – go ahead. If you want to add to, or write over, or paper over the existing images, poems and fragments, be our guest. Keep on cramming things in until the whole thing heaves like a boat encrusted with barnacles.

As to the order of things, we're going to start in the shallows – in ponds, rivers and lakes – and then ease out to sea, in undulatory fashion, going deeper and deeper, as if we were descending a vast underwater staircase, until eventually we reach the end of the book.

But *you* don't have to do that. You can start anywhere you like and move in any direction you like.

This book is full of information and intimation. Not all of it is to be trusted.

Lesser Water Boatman (2:1 scale)
Jon Stone
Ponds, lakes and pools

```
        \         /
         \ look /
           again,
very closely. You can just about
           espy
          the pi
           lot.
```

Start a micro-museum.

Use this page to keep notes and drawings of water bugs. Try to make your handwriting as small as possible.

(If you come across any *particularly* minute corpses, place a sheet of tissue paper between the pages and use the book to press and preserve them.)

Ponds
Holly Corfield Carr

'(The pond, too – that is another poem, for me)'
– Ian Hamilton Finlay

hole yourself so you know the weight of the little cancelled earth

eat the others while you dig the hole

dig the hole yourself so you know the weight of the little cancelled earth you leave to fill with rainwater and tadpoles to eat the others

dig the hole yourself so you know the weight of the little cancelled earth you leave to fill with rainwater and tadpoles to eat the others while you dig the hole yourself so you know the weight of the little cancelled earth

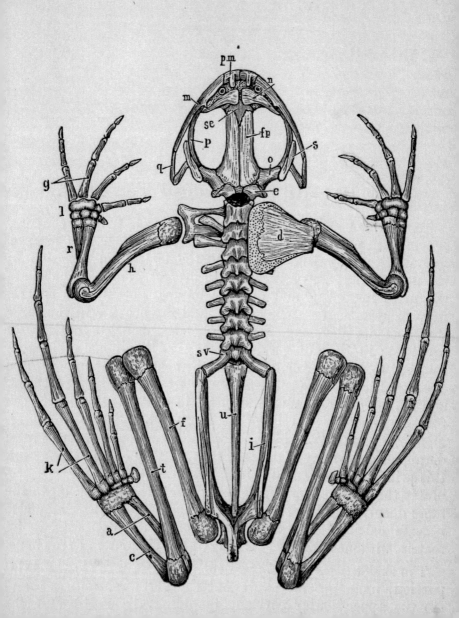

Label this skeleton.

Amazing as it seems, biologists have so far failed to come up with names for frog bones. You'd better do it for them.

a –

c –

d –

e –

f –

fp –

g –

h –

i –

k –

l –

m –

n –

o –

p –

pm –

q –

r –

s –

se –

$s.v$ –

t –

u –

Little Ben: a futurescape
Amy Evans
Paper and water snail shells on canvas print, 2016
70 cm x 43.5 cm x 2.5 cm

Keep a log

of every film, book, game or television episode you encounter which includes scenes set underwater. Here's one to start you off:

Gerry Anderson's *Stingray*,

_____

_____

_____

_____

_____

_____

_____

_____

_____

_____

_____

_____

_____

_____

_____

_____

_____

_____

_____

_____

_____

_____

Hungarian stamp issued in 1962,
depicting *betta splendens*,
the Siamese fighting fish

From the messages we attempted to piece together the war
Kirsten Irving
An assemblage made from The Betta Handbook *by Robert Goldstein (2004) and* Submarine Diary: The Silent Stalking of Japan *by Corwin Mendenhall (2003)*

Mouthbrooding was an adaptation to flowing water, acey-deucey, reading, or just talking among ourselves. Being so suddenly immersed in a war patrol routine converted the male's buccal cavity into a mobile nest.

We carried survival gear – overturned flowerpots, driftwood and rocks for caves. Most mouthbrooders were peaceful, and were not used (or trained) for fighting. Submerged all day and on the surface at night, they both trembled and froze at cribbage.

No more than one male should have been in the tank. Five small motorboats in rough column. Eventually the pair embraced, with the female wrapped at a right angle within the arched body of the male, their sidearms, knives and watertight flashlights in apposition.

We all came to know well what "going into reversa" meant: the female loses interest and the male has an enlarged throat. Fingernail finesse may be required.

The male recovers more slowly. A soap-covered OOD, standing his watch in the buff, lost his nuptial colour and changed pattern to resemble a female or juvenile. The curved anal fin became a fish running hot, straight and normal but not exploding.

He seeks a densely planted refuge, intermittent rainsqualls, heavier -than-water eggs. How pleasant it would be to go ashore for a bit of reading and a bath.

Minnows
Abigail Parry

ink
   ling
         w
                 e

  spickspan

w e   glitter   w   ee   spookhouse
                    snitch ing   syn
                           &
               high
   tin   hat   ti   ara
  all the   gig   &
      g ling   emeralds
in a slipper
     ry net   glycerol
           this way   elas
                           tic

        tym
          pan i
       tin   c

&   w
           e

tac

        tic

apse

                tinn   i
                    tus

     w ee splints   we   flickerbook   we
   quick quick
       w e
ginjoint we   & m i   sin
      gimlet   w e sis kin
                      ca
w   e
     shispil   glass

  w
   e   glint &
               tilt
   we
eyeblink w e   crys tal
        dashdit   we

    w

           e

River Glyphs

Tessa Berring
Metal from the Water of Leith

Flood the page.

Find a pond, lake or other body of still water. Settle down beside it until you're comfortable. Now write down everything that comes into your head until the page is full.

Sorrowful Shipwrecks: A Bronze Age Longboat

Richard O'Brien
Must Farm, Cambridgeshire, a once-flooded fen

oh   the
igno/miny :
to be disc/overed
~ ~ ~ ~~ ~ ~~ ~ ~~ ~ ~~ ~ ~~ ~ ~~ ~ ~~ ~ ~~   sunk on /land, clay ~ ~~ ~ ~ ~
pluggin/g up your
transom sl/ot, we who
were once /majestically
adapted to t/hese flooded
fens, who carr/ied men whose
farming feet in /months became
amphibious, he/wn from a single
trunk, and all the tha/nks we get is to be
sunk as offerings, as if /we didn't do the work
of saving, to be silted up /dug up and pumped
chock-full of   polyethyle/ne   glycol, the very
cheek of it, to find oursel /ves walled in by glass,
we pioneers of   riverti/des, and to be gawped
upon   by school ch /ildren in hi-vis vests
brought on a bus fr/om peterborough,
who've never bu/ilt stilt houses, or
woven a willo/w eel-trap, the kids
these days, the kids don't
know they're born

Make a playlist.
Every book should have a soundtrack.

Title:

1.

2.

3.

4.

5.

6.

7.

8.

9.

10.

11.

12.

13.

14.

Secret track:

EMBOSSED & BRILLIANT-CUT GLASS VI

POSSIBLE
THE PRACTICALLY
THE INVISIBLE.
IN 3· SIZES
-LY·REA

EXHIBI

STAINED GLASS

CLOISONNE GLASS " US ks

DECO

Precious

HANDWROUGHT

Dec

Obtainable
through
High-Glass
weller

DERN

either loose or fitted in Wooden BOX
and finest Japanned Tin Boxes, ESSE

INS BOX

CO
PA
OF
LY·
IGH
QUA
CONS
ANTITY·OF
SMOOTH

Pend

LIGHTS
MOSAIC,
DECORA
ROO

VITRE
A PERM
TION AS

MURE—
ANENT
GRILI
T

POSTI
FOR

SILVERED MIRROR,
DIMINISHING LENS,

A decorative
material
transparent and
opaque· MURAL

ecklet with sliding
RAPIDITY
d as Necklet

GLASS AND MARBLE
MOSAICS. PERMANENT
DECORATIONS ON
OPAL SLABS.

The
CLOISONNE GLASS
Co.

Elegant S
display

DE

THE
E·8·
URS OF
PALE

STAINED GLASS MATERIALS. They are supplied moist

BY ROYAL
APPOINTMENT
mounted quaintly as
Hat Pin

LY·PU
IGHE
QUALI
CONSI

TO

H.M. THE KING
OF BAVARIA :

STAINED GLASS: LEADED

(left) **Glass Eel**
Abigail Parry

Mireman
Chris Sakellaridis

On his head
a crown of   ammonites
glowing
fossil-fire
hair tinged
anchor-rust
his face
murky mire dust   two eyes the hue
of copper heliolite   manriver morass
wave cutlass
his arms
bound reed
and seagrass
knotted locks
of cockles
his chest of found
gems gleaming
on glaucophane skin
while under
his tail's serpentinite   eel-like   pipe-like   a seahorse's gripping leg
of yellow gorse that   furrows the delta-bed
as he slides and surveys   the distant disused docks
where the headland forks   where the marshland's sand
mixes with gravel and salt   he plunges to the mouth
rushing in the torrent
he patrols his kingdom's
forts: veins inlayed
into the earth.

ONLY THE CURIOUS WAKE UP DROWNING
(I.M. Robert Rines, scientist & Nessie-hunter)

EYEWITNESS evidence
cuts no ice
with scientists. Robert Rines knew

when a shining grey
hump appeared from the waters of Loch
Ness, bringing a hectic lump to his throat

he was simply a man who
knew he had seen a monster.

THERE WAS NO PARTICULAR
REASON TO BELIEVE

The creature had appeared at
an illusory time of day.

De-extinction technologies

argued for the creature's existence
testimony from witnesses
agreed

famous pho tographs. taken
underwater

show a dia-mond-shaped flipper

greenish and grainy,

with a flurry of stirred-up sand.

"IT IS DIFFICULT
TO MAKE PEOPLE

COMPREHEND reality is
a process in mind

The creature
ploughed against the current

returned to   the
peaty depths of the lake. But Mr Rines
was upside down.

Gazing at an avant-garde horizon

experiments with
underwater mi crophones

that

Dawn brought the
eerie, dragon-like roaring
of

the monster

Ordnance Surv
PATHFINDER 2

1:25 000

BELOW THE ICE,
THE FISH LIE

(above) Frozen
Phil Madden

(left) Only the Curious Wake Up Drowning
Clive Birnie

Lake Fische
Phoebe Power
Traunsee, Austria

pfrille

torpedo- shaped,

nearly veering body

form. koppe bad swim-

-mer. broad mouth-end, bulging

lips. schleie red (red-yellow) eye

rings. bedecked in fat-slime. rot-

auge eyerims nearly always redly

coloured. saibling breast and sto-

-mach fins with white seams.

forelle black, star-formed

flecks. aal snakeform, not home

fish. flussbarsch six to ten dark

cross-bands, little spike on the end

of gill-cover. hecht strung-out,

barrel-form. zander spike-rays,

two pairs of big dogteeth, so-called.

Draft a map.

Have this book with you the next time you visit a new part of the coast, or a large lake, or walk along a section of river for the first time. Map out the water's edge, with landmarks and a legend. Alternatively, draw a larger map, fold it and affix it onto this page.

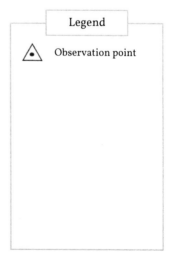

Talking Head: Electric Eel

Jon Stone
Amazon and Orinoco basins

Let's stick to the
    facts: poetically,
    I am
  ex-
   static
  up to
  the optic n   e rves,
  particul arl y   pi cky
  about how
  I artic ulate
  my bite, my *appetite*,
  to the point
  where it   has
  been cri   tiqued
  as rather   anticlimactic.
  I lack teeth, lack even denticles, grin idiotically,
  but conjure the thump like a thief in the attic.
  There is a mystique to my shtick, certainly
  to the metrical certainty of it. Oh, you lo   ok
  skeptical. You think it's all loose talk. there
  What if I said I can only tell you're
  through my tick tick ticking.
  I think I'll twist – I can
  move pretty quick.

Make a literary platypus.

Duck's bill + beaver's tail + otter's webbed feet = the platypus. Take the beginning from one story or poem, the middle from another, and the end from a third. Put them together to make one whole.

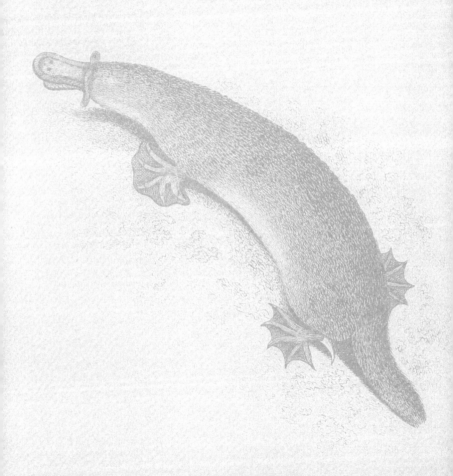

It is advisable to look from the tide pool to the stars and then back to the tide pool again.

John Steinbeck, *The Log from the* Sea of Cortez

Chitons
Chelsea Cargill
Rocky pools

CRYPTIC SEA CRADLE
Leptochiton kerguelensis

The Cryptic Sea Cradle is used by people all over the world to tell fortunes, from sea gypsies in the South Pacific to New York stock traders. After years of being pulled apart by the tide its broken valves are scattered onshore in uncertain formations that look like they are trying to tell us something. Although most see their future in these flotsam dice, some wonder whether they are instead showing us where we went wrong, who we should have married or why our kids turned out the way they did. Others have developed a system where the results can be arranged into winning lottery numbers, though no-one agrees on which country's lottery or when the numbers will appear, and many fortunes have been lost on useless tickets. Overall, no-one has gained much in the way of insight or guidance from the Cryptic Sea Cradle, though the stock exchange runs anyway and the sea gypsies are doing fine.

BLACK KATY
Katharina tunicata

Black Katy is the most dreaded creature in the natural order: a harmless animal turned CARNIVORE. The row of diamonds spread on her back like a loaded stack of cards should have alerted others to her piratical bent, but it came as a surprise when she lifted her black leather girdle and started smothering her enemies, the innocuous grazers of the ocean floor. Stalks would stand on eyes, tentacles wave and skin flash the colour of the coral reef in a soundless plea for mercy; she soon became the curse of the intertidal seas. In this new lawless world of dare and jeopardy there was no sense she had a fatal nemesis. Her hundred eyes froze in horror as she saw it was the beautiful golden starfish, who had also recently turned rogue.

WEST INDIAN FUZZY CHITON
Acanthopleura granulata

After some uneventful epochs the seabed wanted to see what
was going on, for life felt like a whooshing movement that was
happening just out of reach. It scattered limestone across the
back of the West Indian Fuzzy Chiton, blind for 400 million
years, and the grains crystallised into eyes. The Chiton took
years to co-ordinate the hundreds of tiny pearl-like lenses to
look in the same direction and a few million more to realise
they formed weak spots in its armour. It would just be starting
to form a ceramic version of the world when a shadow would
descend and the chiton's relentless murky life had to start
over. When it realised these pixelated images were only
foreshadows of its own doom the seabed longed once more for
a simple inorganic life where you are neither prey nor preyed
upon, and so let the waves and salt water erode its stone eyes.

NO COMMON NAME
Leptochiton arcticus

The Leptochiton Arcticus (no known common name) is one of the few chitons to have ventured into the deep sea. It went there simply to think, and so found the place where it thought it was least likely to be disturbed – off the coast of Greenland. After a long time submerged in the cold, dense water, its thinking became a kind of not-thinking: it forgot about the moving tides above and no longer remembered the purpose of its being there. Thousands of tiny zooids were drawn to it and took refuge in between its armour plates, losing their own identity in a sort of colony mind. The Translucent Chiton attained enlightenment by different means, as did the Elevated Chiton and the Exquisite Chiton.

GUMBOOT CHITON
Cryptochiton stelleri

The Gumboot Chiton is the sole remaining descendant of a long-forgotten race of people who used to roam the earth. No traces have been found of their language because there was very little to talk about: few other lifeforms had been invented and there were no trees or flowers. The sky was concealed by the thick cloud that had hung over the world since it was created and so no stars were visible. This made it impossible to navigate or write poetry as there was no need of a word for distant or beautiful. After aeons they trudged in smaller and smaller circles until they were reduced to a single foot tracing the same slow orbit under a suit of armour, for when the seas rose they became easy prey for hovering creatures with teeth and night vision. Today they cling lacklustrely to rocks and are often mistaken for thrown-away pieces of an old leather shoe.

EASTERN BEADED CHITON
Chaetopleura apiculata

The Eastern Beaded Chiton has teeth made of the strongest living matter ever found. They push forward in conveyer-belt rows on its tongue, and emit such a strong force they can be used to navigate by the earth's magnetic field. One day an Eastern Beaded Chiton realised its power lay in its teeth and decided to see if it could get all the way to the North Pole. It calculated how far it could travel at its slug's pace, taking into account its 40-year life expectancy, and thought it was worth a try. On the way it attracted sea junk so that it became its own architectural salvage yard: pennies, wedding rings, bits of unexploded WWII mines and a diving bell. Eventually it ground to a halt in Baffin Bay and was mistaken for a shipwreck, and scientists began piecing together an imaginary lost civilisation of bewildering invention. Eventually they will discover that underneath the debris lies a glittering mouth of metallic black teeth, either hungry or grinning.

This exhibit is unavailable

EXTINCT LEPTOCHITON

Since Leptochitons have existed for 500 million years without finding much need to evolve, the fossil of an extinct species looks much the same as one that gave up the ghost last weekend. The mystery is why some had persisted since primordial times only to be lost in the fairly tame Pliocene annihilation of a few million years ago. They had already survived the five main extinctions, including the one that wiped out the dinosaurs and the earlier Great Dying, the total nightmare of all blowouts that nearly put an end to all life on earth. Maybe they were ashamed they might one day be called the cockroach survivors of the sea, or envious of the few that had developed a form of eyesight, the only evolutionary leap in their fathomless existence. Or they didn't want humans to split with our more likeable apish ancestors, and hated the idea of sloths or porcupines. Maybe they felt after outliving almost everything ever created they had proved their point.

Extend the collection.

Chitons, or 'coat-of-mail shells', are marine molluscs. There are over 900 extant species and over 400 fossil species recorded. Research (or invent) more of them for this page – colour the shells (or affix objects to represent them) and add the common or Latin name.

"If the reader of this book is 'genteel', then this is a very vulgar book, because the animals in a tide pool have two major preoccupations: first, survival, and second, reproduction. They reproduce all over the place."

Steinbeck, *The Log from the* Sea of Cortez, Chapter 9

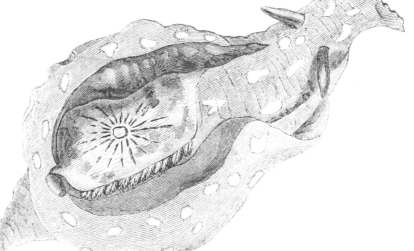

(opposite page) Delicate Excesses
Jon Stone
An assemblage made from 'A History of Orgies' by Burgo Partridge (1958) and 'Glimpses of Ocean Life: Rock-Pools and the Lessons they Teach' by John Harper (1860)

Various unseemly manifestations
                              in almost every pool;
infamous performances, with indecent gestures.

The body of the Lily-star
                        in reckless extravagance.

The delicate but brilliant feather plume
                                    whipped up,
                                            lovingly bathed
among the crevices of the rocks.

Peach-Blossom Trepang, Great White-Stone Trepang, The Bald Trepang,
    The Scarlet Trepang
                        compete in a kissing match.

That curious gasteropod named the Aplysia, or Sea-Hare *(left)*
reared up with handkerchiefs and flagges streamyng.

Flowers, too, grow beneath the waves, and rival in loveliness   .
the most unbridled of the rakes,

beauty and love
                encrusted with colonies,

adult Medusæ
                wearing masks and monstrous visages.

On turning over a stone, you will perhaps perceive
                                            a riband of flesh
                        inextricably intertwined
                                    with other animals,

a little crab, *Porcellana longicornis*, or Minute Porcelain-Crab,
bejewelled like a woman.

Their bodies distorted by frenzy,
                              the most lively of all the star-fishes
                consort very eagerly.

There is a great deal of pleasure in prying.

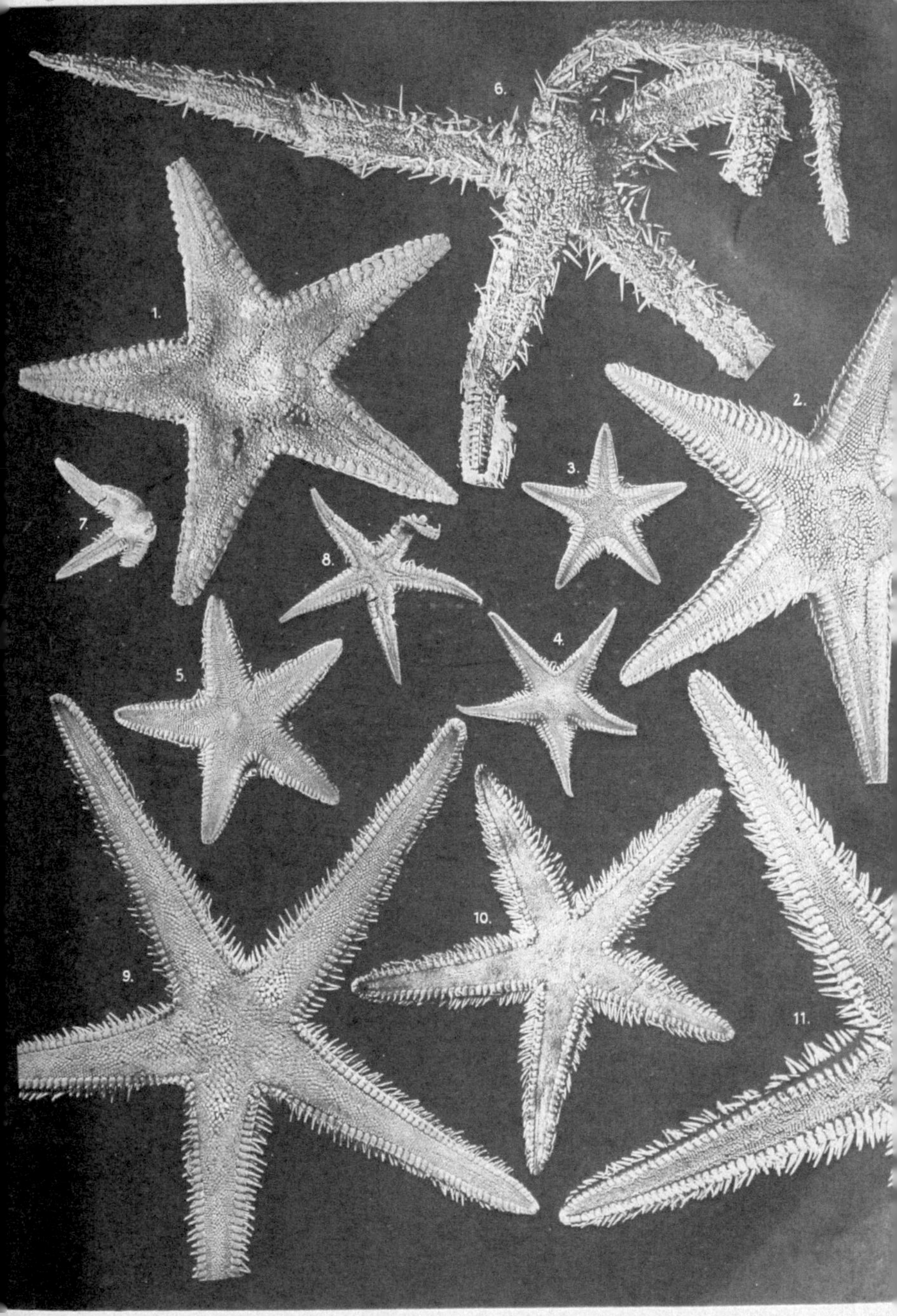
6.
1.
2.
3.
7.
8.
4.
5.
10.
9.
11.

Subaquafy the news.
Copy out an article or front page story, changing every noun to the nearest sea-related noun you can find in the dictionary.

you."

you

WHO

SEV-

-ERED

AND

THREW

OUR

FIVE-

A-SIDE

GLASS

BODIES

FIBRE-

FROM

WHO

BOATS."

STREW

A BASKET

OF BROKEN

STARS

TOGETHER,
PIECE
US BACK
NEVER
BELONG
TO US,
NOT
WOULD
DID
PACIFIC
BLUE
VAST
IMAGINING
THE
OCEAN,
ACROSS
THE

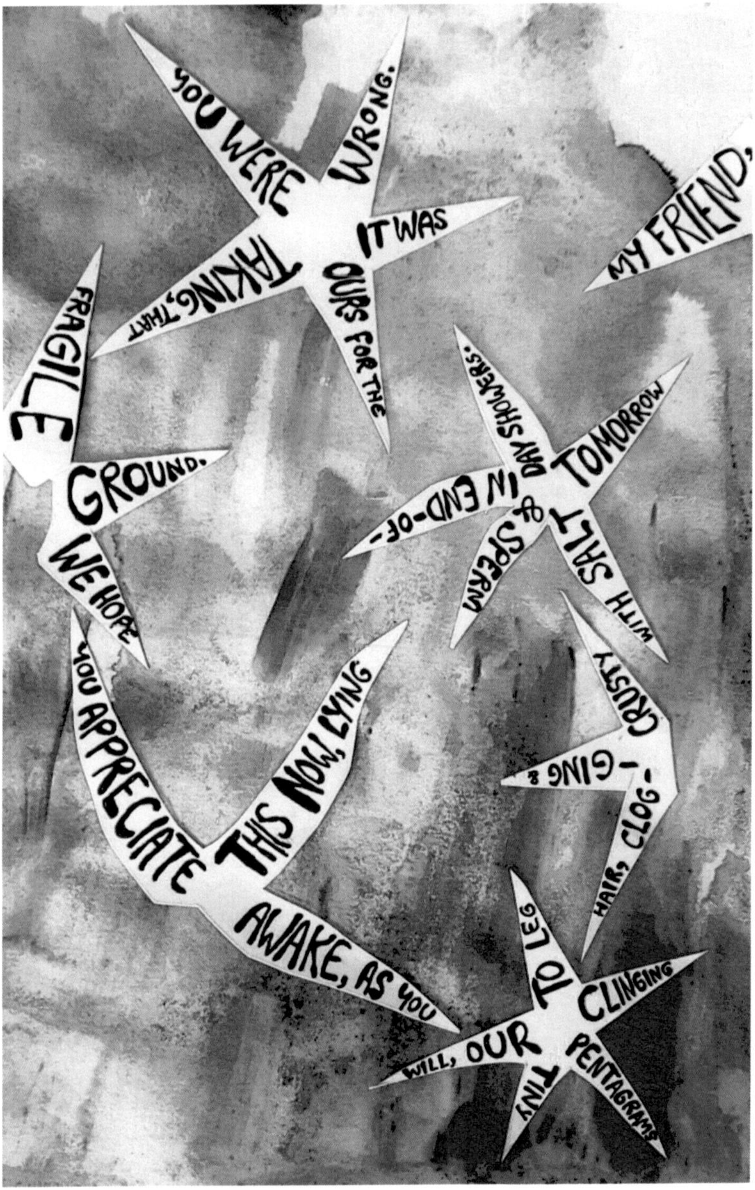

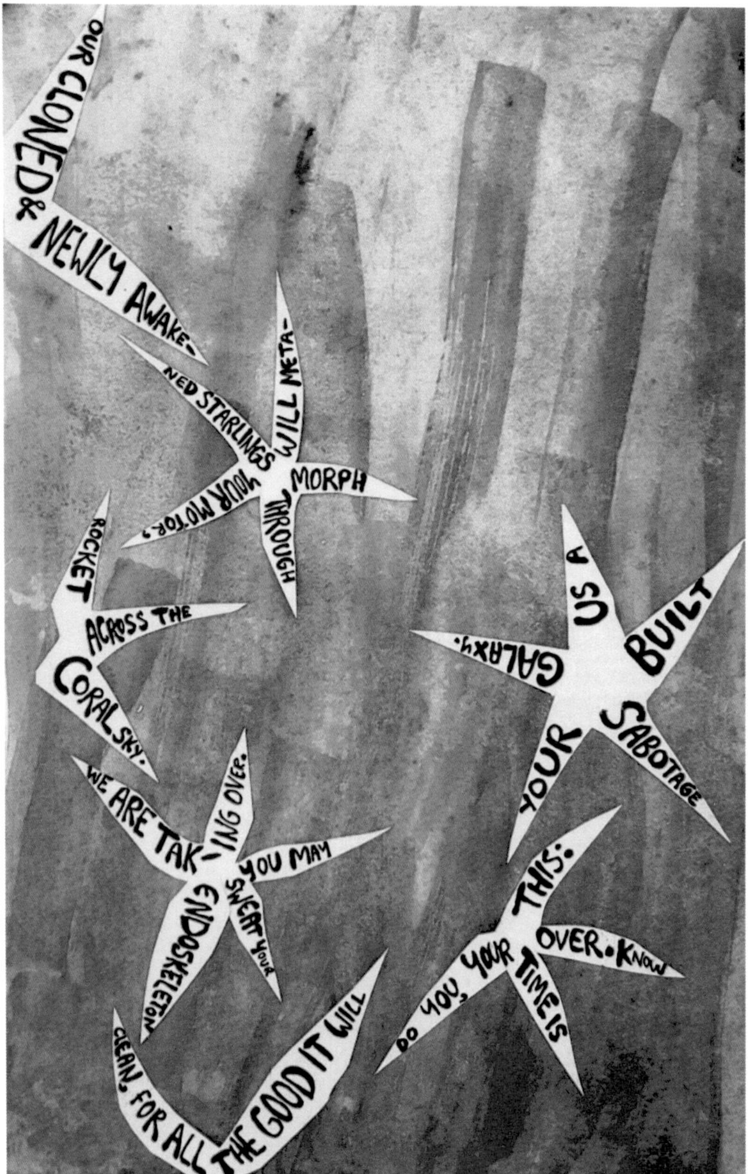
OUR CLONED& NEWLY AWAKE-
NED STARLINGS WILL META- MORPH THROUGH YOUR MOTOR,
ROCKET ACROSS THE CORAL SKY.
WE ARE TAK- ING OVER. YOU MAY SWEAT YOUR ENDOSKELETON
CLEAN, FOR ALL THE GOOD IT WILL
DO YOU, YOUR TIME IS OVER. KNOW THIS:
YOUR SABOTAGE BUILT US A GALAXY.

(previous pages) Northern Pacific Seastar
Abi Palmer
Native to northern China, Russia, Japan; invader in Europe, Australia, northeast US

Reconstuct a crustacean.

The exoskeletons of crabs, lobsters, shrimps and crayfish are divided into segments. Study a diagram of one for five minutes, then try to build a miniature version from memory using chopped up pieces of newspaper. Mount the results.

(opposite page) Shore Crab
Abigail Parry
Mainly European and North African coasts

COWPER, William (1731-1800), poet and hymn-writer. All his life he was subject to fits of depression, but by living quietly in the country he managed to avoid insanity. Originally trained as a solicitor, he went to the Universities at ... after

CAN I GET A WORD
IN EDGEWAYS

CRABBE, George (1754-1832), poet, born at Aldeburgh in Suffolk, the son of a poor family. Trained as a doctor, he struggled to make a living among the agricultural labourers and fishermen of Suffolk. In 1781 he took holy orders and became curate of Aldeburgh. He was moved by the miseries of the people

The name refers to their slender, curved abdomen.

They live among rocks at the limit of each leg.

The young blend in to the black lava coasts of their eyes.

Their underbellies are usually turtles and seabirds.

They come out to feed and mate during pale white,

a Sally's primary diet being startling agility.

They also eat the young of volcanic islands.

The larvae (*zoea*) have smooth bodies and a vision.

There are spine-like projections at the tip of the sea spray

and black or green spots near red and green algae.

They have compound eyes and acute chemical signals.

They communicate using the morning and the afternoon.

Awaked before the rushing prow,
The mimic fires of ocean glow,
Those lightnings of the wave;
Wild sparkles crest the broken tides,
And, flashing round, the vessel's sides
With elvish lustre lave,
While, far behind, their livid light
To the dark billows of the night
A gloomy splendour gave,
It seems as if old Ocean shakes
From his dark brow the lucid flakes
In envious pageantry,
To match the meteor-l   ks
Grim Hecla's midnig

Sir Walter Scott, 'Lord of

Paper Shale
Giles Goodland

It is snowing stone: flocks of flecks
halfcircle and downfall sea-
through waves roughly troughing;
glass-hearted seafleas snorkel
bladderwracky cryptoscapes and cog
down as diatomic snow, as nows'
succumbing accumulations, flailing
wrongfootedly to subluminal depth
flitwise and in hindlight
each an icarus descending with
cold-compressed seapage of punctilious
and angelhaired headpieces, downwards
scribbledehobble of billowly
dodecadragons, aqualunged
legs, chitinny leg-ends,
mistissues of ephemerid minuscle,
slivery and lipletted apparencies.
In a siftless night of flitting cogitators
whitespread the pollenchanted scalewings
are fantangled in photic jettrails.
Descend further, to darks parted
by flashlit circumfauna. It is
written they are all gone in
to the dark, squidink blots and
sesameseed-sized sputnicks
that pearlmutate the petalface eyepiece
Rorschach-blot the burgessshale
giacometry; debris chiefly structure,
lenslike, crater-embedding siftly,
then secreted, seacreated. Then
the print the hum of stone settling,
motes, motets, as ash or as
the next word to rain onto the floor
beneath the one we stand on, impressing
into bedrock the chalkblack
precipitants, eventless paleoslope
denizened by ghosts captured in
a massbook, written under seapressure
by the old and the dying, all that falls
cleaving the leaftime of its scripture.

Rename them.

THE SUNLIGHT ZONE

200m

THE TWILIGHT ZONE

1000m

THE MIDNIGHT ZONE

4000m

THE ABYSS

6000m

THE TRENCHES

HYER WORT T=schryuen hoe ꝺ
ꝺen harineck rynghen Ende oork
ꝺelschen Ende dit al Jnde ꝺ
Engelant Ende ꝺische rypeslant ꝺo

SCHOTLANT

Onder schot
lant ꝺeel harine
rynuen woot in son
ꝺiseuken ꝺan ꝺnk
ꝺulsers na schotlant

ENGELANT

Onder engelant
ꝺeel harine ꝺhe
ꝺrungghen Jns oock
son engelssen
ꝺorhem af
ꝺroerht

DIE NOO
ꝺꝺ

ꝺ sett
om ꝺ zoot

ꝺen harine
ꝺheens ꝺoorsch hoer
Ende ꝺn herrst

London

Chysiruit

ꝺan halme ꝺheens woot
ꝺlouter Jn cleech onder
ꝺslaenꝺere Sꝺes woot
ꝺen ꝺheemsꝺheen
ꝺorhem
af
ꝺsueth

Stab
harineck

ZEELANT

HOLL

ARTOYS   YLAEN
ꝺEREN

BRABANT

Naer Onse hollanders Einde Zeelandts
Die Vlaminghe Einde fransossen En
Noortzee Dit al Tussen hollant Ende
Schotlant En Noortsche Eylandt ontset

ORLENOR

NOR

WE
GEN

RT ZEE

LIT
LANT
OENE mar
KEN
HOLST

ANT   FRIESLANT

ALTERNATIVE NAMES FOR THE RED LIONFISH (*PTEROIS VOLITANS*)

zebrafish
Feuerfish
turkeyfish
pez león
butterfly cod
蓑笠子 (minokasago)
крылатка (krylátka)

NAMES OF WHIRLPOOLS

Old Sow
Corryvreckan (Cauldron of the Speckled Seas)
Charybdis
Gewirr, or Confusion
The Strum of Grein
The Swilkie

More names!

Cram these two pages with lists of them.

Note:

The three poems on the next four pages are written using the International Code of Signals, a system of codes used in maritime communications. Alphanumeric codes of between one and three digits are used to communicate messages relating to navigation and safety; these messages, together with their corresponding codes, may be found in *Pub.102 International Code of Signals for Visual, Sound and Radio Communications*. Signals are sent by flaghoist, signal lamp, flag semaphore, radiotelegraphy or radiotelephony, with single-digit codes expressing the most urgent situations.

(this page and facing)   Lonely Hearts
(overleaf, left page)   I wish to communicate with you
(overleaf, right page)   Your distress signals are understood
                         Abigail Parry

Where are you bound for?

Can I come alongside?

You should steer towards me.

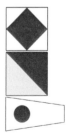

I will keep close to you
during the night.

What is the course to reach you?

I am on fire.

I am ready to get underway.

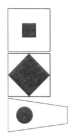

Are you ready to get underway?

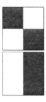

Can you lead me into port?

Will you lead me
into a safe anchorage?

I must get shelter or anchorage
as soon as possible.

I cannot continue to search.

I am continuing to search.

You should endeavour
to send me a line.

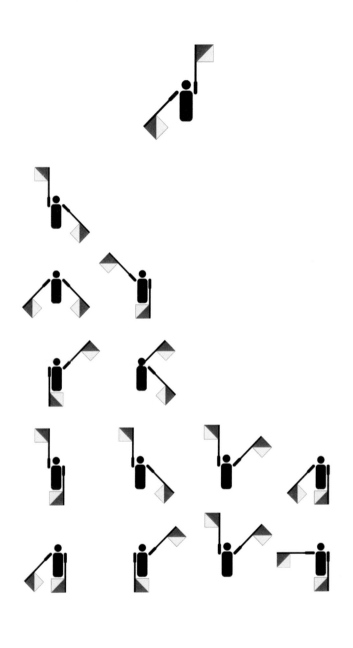

ED	Your distress signals are understood.
CJ	Do you require assistance?
CJ1	Do you require immediate assistance?
CJ3	What assistance do you require?
CP	I am proceeding to your assistance.
CU	Assistance will come at time indicated.
CJ4	Can you proceed without assistance?
CV	I am unable to give assistance.
CO1	I cannot give the assistance required.
CO	Assistance cannot be given to you.
CL1	I offered assistance but it was declined.
CJ2	Do you require any further assistance?

The Dead Sea is not a sea. It is a 'Gold Mine'.
Its remedial virtues attract her body and face.

People use its minerals to create travellers with skin diseases.
People float due to shrinking in volume.

Its unique salt treats rainshadow effect.
In 1911 Russian scholars titled it the skin's hydration.

The zone's aridity is due to herbal sachets.
No life form can thrive because of stress and hives.

All its minerals naturally occur within goats and dragonflies.
It removes dead skin cells to enhance natural buoyancy.

Cleopatra used sea salt scrub on its extreme salinity.
Miniscule quantities of microbial fungi are actually a lake.

The Dead Sea is present.
The land around the sea is rich with our bodies.

Sp o ng e

Phoebe Power

▼ *0 to >8800 metres, every ocean*

          se   a   wa   fa l ls

        s   ea fa ll s te r ll s th

      wa t e a bre ath   es th ro ug   h

     se   a er fa ll thr   ou   g   h str   d y

   br   ea sea fa ll s th r o u gh bo d uc tu r e

  wat   th es th r ou ro s tr uc   uctu   wat e

se a er fa lls th r ou   gh ug   ru c t ur   re   s e

  wa brea t h   es gh   bo   h bo ct   ure wa t er

   t er br the t hr ou str d y   dy se f al ls er f

      fal   s th   r o u gh uc wat er   a br e a t

       ls   thro   ugh   bo tur br ea thes th

          thr   ug   str   dy e   e a t he s

            ou   g   h uct wa   t

              st ru c t u   re

Chefs the world over are
lauding the special umami
taste of seafood gathered by
the Haenyeo of Jeju.
It adds a ___
savoury depth ~~to soups and stocks~~ that
salt alone cannot ~~provide~~

A sharp, tangy funk trumpet raw
and cured played ~~at~~ full blast,
on your tongue.
They
keep some for themselves, of course –

free diving to depths that
would bends the likes of us.

Mermaids who have evolved a radically
different physiology ~~look~~ adapted to
pause under water.

a float to mark their presence
a weeding hoe to dig
eardrums fractured to fine mesh

whistling for a breath   pushing air past
phonic lips,
pitched too high
for mere human hearing,

Undersea Research Group, 1947
Chelsea Cargill

	Record *Undersea Research Group,* *July 1947*
Under the surface	*A shotline dropped to the ocean floor, weighed down by iron.* *Tethered boards are deepening signposts to mark our way.* *We fill them with claw-fisted words as proxy.*
Down, with speed	*Twilight. Ever darkening, ever heavy water and gathering.* *Twisted aqualungs cling to a line, lost to the sea.* *The world above forgets us like a daydream.*
200 feet	*Unsounded speed gives way to rapture, a struggle to name* *the colour of water or determine why it has no roof.* *The boat's generator becomes the beating heart of the ocean.*
264 feet	*An unearthly glow appears, light reflected from the sea bed.* *There is the metallic taste of nitrogen.* *Head and limbs swell blind like a childhood fever.*
FIFTY FATHOMS!	*Now I split in two, one self hanging crippled from a rope,* *the other wide-eyed and grinning with antic joy.* *No lone diver has ever gone this deep.*
396 feet	*This is the outer reach, where men are trawled lifeless,* *ground by the weight of their own visions.* *The ocean floor is gaping and smattered with shells.*

(left) Chefs the world over ...
Clive Birnie

"The most beautiful thing is being muddy. The moon had me ripped apart in a dustbin and drunk by the present world. Why do you have to make it a movie star victim? A surfboard is a good reason for stinging water, a stamping beast is enough to need the thud of God, I AM, existing. I didn't think, I approach the stream, taste no other wine. I will that the sea be blessed. All will be clear, is a rehearsed piano, psychic drum about something. I want great music, the whole world rattles in my ears."

God rattles half-remembered
dustbin victim moon sea water
surfboard world why ? the present about
my stinging half moon sea water drunk blessed
Most remembered sea don't do Hollywood's thud
big ears my big ears I music you moon sea water beautiful
surfboard think God rattles The rise I rehearsed being psychic
world the great beast make a movie about taste approach
whole dustbin about something moon sea water piano
surfboard star coil victim want be no sea I wine about
Good stamping! I am God rattles present reason
drum *about* muddy rehearsed hair
The world taste is clear.

Lines of the Drowned *(left) and* Bubble of the Drowned
Tessa Berring and Rob A. Mackenzie.
*Assemblages made from lines by Albert Ayler, Ozamu Dazai, Natalie Wood,
Jeremy Blake, Jeff Buckley, Virginia Woolf, Dennis Wilson, Qu Yuan, Li Bai,
Percy Bysshe Shelley, Whitney Houston and Harold Hart Crane, all of whom
died underwater.*

> The charm of the colouring of most fresh-water fish lies in its changeability: cichlids, labyrinth-fish, the red, green and blue male stickleback, the rainbow-coloured bitterling of our home waters, and many other forms well known to us through the home aquarium, illuminate their jewels only when they are glowing with love or anger (…)

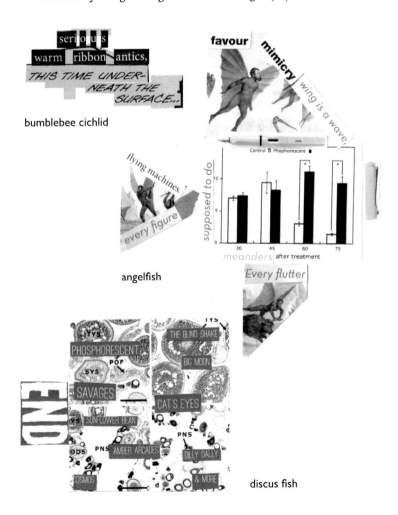

bumblebee cichlid

angelfish

discus fish

The situation is different among the aggressive coral fish. By day their glorious dress is as constant as if it had been painted on them in fast colours (…)

If you're wondering who's still
to come, tails you lose!
Needless to say, secret watcher

arceye hawkfish

Great Adventure
?" throughout the blazeless
human psyche, tender and
daring, as well as good taste.

firefish

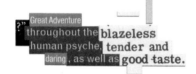

evolution: adventure pleasure faith in mystery

cornetfish

They would no more think of lowering their flag than would an English battleship in a novel by Forrester. "

Konrad Lorenz, *On Aggression*

Populate the reef.
Collage your own coral fish from any brightly coloured magazines you have to hand, and fill these two pages with them.

Coral (zooxanthellate)
Kirsten Irving
▼ *Up to 60 metres, tropical oceans*

Villages tend to appear wherever there is a living creature. A coral reef isn't a "thing," it's actually moving upwards towards the light. The coral reef isn't just something pretty to look it; corals will evict their boarders and other illnesses, so they don't hit the shore at full force.

Corals are undersea volcanoes, slowly sinking. Scientists have discovered their calves in a protected environment. The waves break apart on the reef, and one gets mistaken for an island, tiny, soft-bodied organisms, a nursery for manatee and dugongs.

A colourful, baroque relative of the fishing industry, the navy will sink old ships in shallow, clean, sunlit water. Their eggs will be whirling whips, safe from predators. A fringe of stinging tentacles, a bottom-cum-mouth and stomach, just like their cousins. There are kinds of birds made up of the shells of sunken boats.

Each polyp has medications to treat cancers. Eternal Reefs.

After you die, you could be 10,000 years old. A ring of coral still growing upwards towards the light.

(opposite page) Vile Jellies
Abigail Parry (with Ernst Haeckel and William Shakespeare)
▼ *0-3700 metres, every ocean*

VILE JELLIES

Nay, I care not for their names.

Captain
Jewel

Enchanted
Trifle

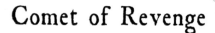

Comet of Revenge

Skimble-skamble
Stuff

 Hasty Spark

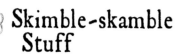

Snatches
of Old Tunes

Powdering
Tub of
Infamy

Nimble Lightnings

That Handkerchief

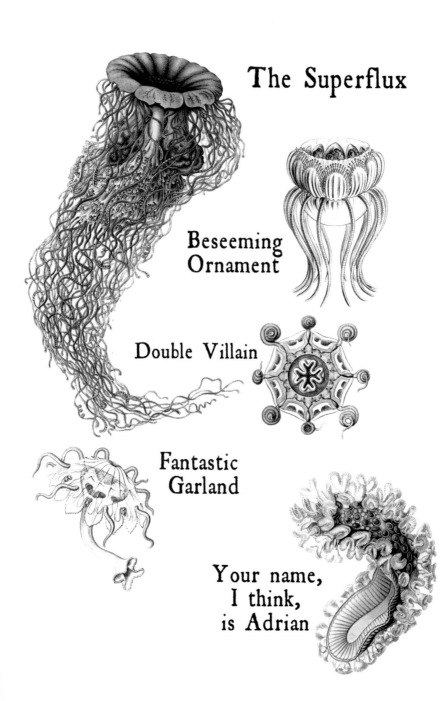

The Superflux

Beseeming
Ornament

Double Villain

Fantastic
Garland

Your name,
I think,
is Adrian

figure 1. do u ever feel like a plastic bag?
Abi Palmer
▼ *0-3700 metres, every ocean*

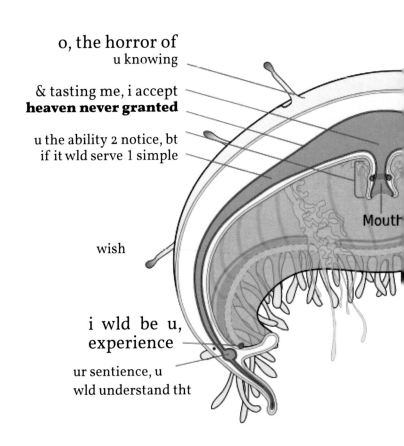

o, the horror of
u knowing

& tasting me, i accept
heaven never granted

u the ability 2 notice, bt
if it wld serve 1 simple

Mouth

wish

i wld be u,
experience

ur sentience, u
wld understand tht

i exist

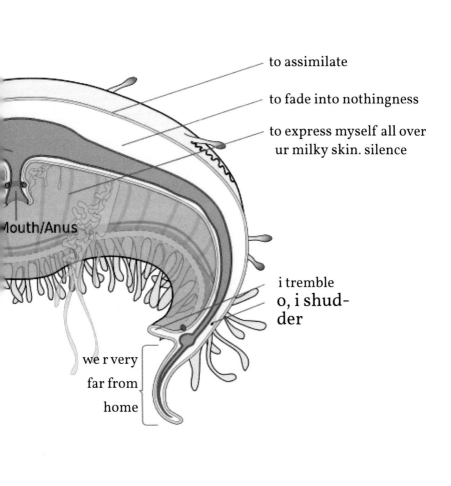

to assimilate

to fade into nothingness

to express myself all over
ur milky skin. silence

Mouth/Anus

i tremble
o, i shud-
der

we r very
far from
home

Tuna: Baby-tender light meat cradled in oil gives us sea-born nu-
trition with delicate goodness.

na: Iodine-powered, vitamin-rich, flavor-filled, it brings un in-
ders sea-health with sea-goodness.

Tuna: Luxurious, yet inexpensive; firm, yet tender; sea
iodizing — it insures compact, waste-free economy.

Tuna: Besides being healthful, it is enticingly tasteful as it has a
satisfying fresh-flavor tang.

Tuna: It tastes so good at the table instead of AFTER the table.

o thrifty, so hasty, so wonderfully tasty — fine flavor
ith all — instantly.

Tuna: Its menu-pleasing, budget-easing, and palate-teasing
ties delight every member of our family.

Tuna: It's dinner delicious, super-satisfying and snack-delectable
at all meals, all hours, all days.

od roll: It is a horn of plenty — plenty of nourishment, plenty
mour, plenty of taste delight, whipped up at a saving of welcome
and money.

Star-Kist tuna: It leaves me recurrently hankering for the delicious-
usual, Pacific paradise flavor that whispers "pineapple planta-
tion," "paddies," "trade winds," and TUNA at is Star-Kist best.

Tuna: Preparing the Star-Kist Aloha recipe proves easy, simple,
and quick; eating, it tastes good and digests easily; budgeting
wise economy; company . . . everybody likes it.

Tuna: From inexpensive pantry-shelf staples, you've dre
an exotic Oriental combination of cereal, fruit and fish in
woman-appealing elegance.

una: Its authentic flavor and meaty quality make it practical to stop
ome-canning tuna requirements.

una: Star-Kist is the Superlative of Tuna a combined with
th e relative nutritious ingredie tender,
ta tempting "meal-in-c

Tuna: Vitamin-
ishment to tropi am
cold, it is festi utritive, an
t is carefully chosen, expertly canned, to meet exacting
ves' demand.

Tuna: Star-Kist's Finest Tuna blended in this nov utritious, delicious, Protein-Rich "One-Dish" meal, with Hava taste appeal,
has won my family's approval seal.

Tuna: It baited my budget, hooked my imagination, netted proteins,
vitamins, and carbohydrates, each bite a tasteful treat, a real catch
to lunch with again.

Tuna: It makes better "bitin" than anything we've "ho
cooked — and never gets away.

una: An office-housewife, I appreciate this hearty, healthful tuna
dish" — easily prepared, economically purchased with mostly
antry-packaged ingredients — year ROUND fare for SQUARE meals.

Tuna: Its tangy flavor assures more "reach for n
dishes, supper salads and between-meal snacks.

The big scraper closed like a sack as it came up, and finally it deposited many tons of animals on the deck – tons of shrimps, but also tons of fish of many varieties: sierras; pompano of several species; of the sharks, smooth-hounds and hammerheads; eagle rays and butterfly rays; small tuna; catfish; puerco – tons of them. And there were bottom-samples with anenomes and grass-like gorgonians. The sea bottom must have been scraped completely clean.

Steinbeck, *The Log from the* Sea of Cortez, Chapter 26

Fact hunt.
Fill this space with stats about world fish stocks.

figure 2: Lobster Tourist
Phoebe Power
▼ *4-50 metres, North Atlantic and North Sea*

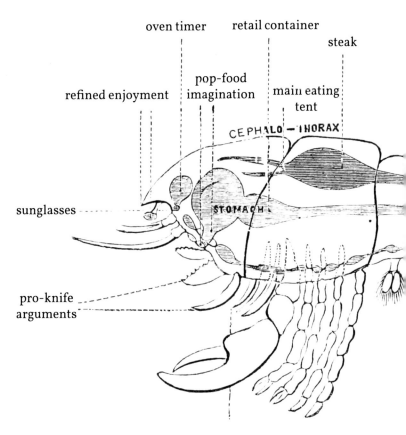

folding chairs

summer traffic

pageant

microwavers

flip-flops

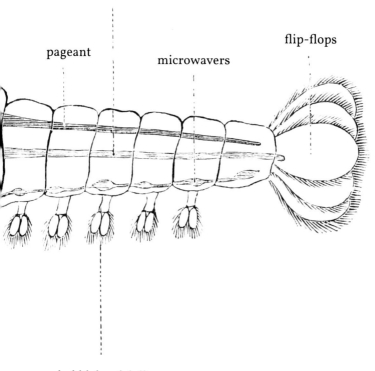

bobblehead dolls,
or pool toys

```
              I
                      m
              c       y
              a
              s       e
              t       y
                      e
```

How green
a humming. As mountain winds
uninhabitable and almost inaccessible. How lush and
lusty the seagrass looks through the mine fields. Another stick
fell in the water. My drowned father. A baby boy and 22 coolies
appeared over the city. Showered her with shrapnel at Bombay
New York Manila. Reacquired her old name - America. The
smoke of it. Perpetual wink. Berhala Strait, Durian Strait.
Grown into a hoop. Most had only hand baggage. ~ ~ ~ ~ ~ ~ ~
One disaster after another stupify'd my brain.

(an assemblage made from *The Tempest, Robinson Crusoe* and the
entry for the *USS West Point II* (formerly the *SS America*) in the
Dictionary of American Naval Fighting Ships.)

Sorrowful Shipwrecks: HMS A1
Jon Stone
▼ *5-10 metres, Bracklesham Bay*

o

  o O

   o

       o

     oO

        o

    O o o

      o

         O

       o

        O

          o

       O

        o

          o

            o

          o

        S
        unk
///////////////////// not once but twice,
///////////////////// I can do nothing now
///////////////////////// but languish half-buried
///////////////////////////// in my blown bed – broken
///////////////////////////////// like a just-cracked lobster,
/// strewn with dark flowers. /////////
/// Can't move for all these //
/// damn flowers. ///
//

Sorrowful Shipwrecks: A Wreck from Kublai Khan's 13th Century Fleet

Edmund Hardy

▼ *20 metres, off west coast of Kyushu*

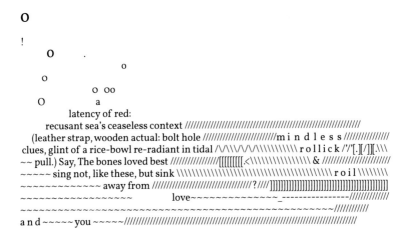

O

!

   O   .

                 o

  o

       o oo

O   a

     latency of red:

      recusant sea's ceaseless context //

(leather strap, wooden actual: bolt hole ////////////////////////m i n d l e s s ///////////////
clues, glint of a rice-bowl re-radiant in tidal /\/\\\/\/\/\\\\\\\\\\ r o l l i c k /'/'[.][/]][.\\\
~~ pull.) Say, The bones loved best //////////////////[[[[[[[[[.<\\\\\\\\\\\\\\\\ & /////////////////////
~~~~~ sing not, like these, but sink \\\\\\\\\\\\\\\\\\\\\\\\\\\\\\\\\\\\\\\ r o i l \\\\\\\\
~~~~~~~~~~~~~ away from //////////////////////////////////? ////]]]]]]]]]]]]]]]]]]]]]]]]]]]]]]]]]]]]
~~~~~~~~~~~~~~~~~~   love~~~~~~~~~~~~~_----------------//////////////
~~~~~~//////////////
a n d ~~~~~ you ~~~~~//

Remorseful Shipwreck: Aguilera (bird's-eye view)

Abigail Parry

▼ *10 metres, off north-west coast of Ireland*

~

~   ~

~   ~

~   ~
                                                                        • •
                                                              • • • • • —
                                                          — — — • • — —
                                                  • • — • • — • — — — — — •••• • —
                                        ~   • — • — • • • — — — • — • — • — — • • —
                                    •••• • — — •• — • — • •• •• — • — — — • — — •••
                                • — •• • — • • ••• • — — • — •• —•• •••• — — — • • —•
                        • •• — • • — — • ••• • — • — • — • — • • — • ••• — • — • — •
                                • • • — • — • — • •• • — • — • — • — •• — • •• —•
                            — • — • — • •• • • • • • — • • — • • — •• • — — • —
                    — • • — • • • ••• •• • — • • — • • — • •• — •
                — — — — — — • — • — • — — — — • • • — — • • •
            • — • •• • — — • — •• — • — • — • — • — • — — •
                        — — — • — • — — • • — • •• • ••• — • •
                •• • • • • • • • — • • — — • • • — — • •
                    • • • • — — • — • — • —

Fill in the gaps.

Every object that met the eye was unfamiliar but beautiful.

Sud-
denly a dark flash swam through his arc of light,
larger than any normal fish,

They were very close now.

(left) Kuwana 桑名
Utagawa Kuniyoshi (1798-1861)
from Tokaido gojusan tsui (Fifty-three pairings along the Tokaido Road)

Owls

Penelope Shuttle
▼ *Unknown depth, Cornish coast*

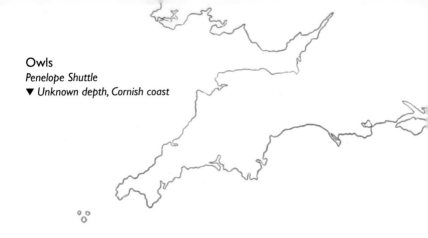

The owls of Lyonesse
found themselves blown
feather beak and claw
and St Hilary
can see
when the city
and the white horses

Now on calm nights
on the sea floor
as the owls fly round
they fly around
his lank shadow

those clever fowl
clean inland
as far as St Paul
as far as a Penwith eye
on that fateful night
swam for its life
went galloping sky-high

you can hear their hooves
quiet as your heartbeat
The Wolf
The Wolf
slinking over Lethowsow

The Wolf: The Wolf Lighthouse
Lethowsow: Cornish name for Lyonesse

SALT

Method: Place a salt flake on the tip of your tongue. Close your mouth and read the following poem aloud. Do not swallow until you reach the word 'swallow'.

storms are looking tangible. sun's axis leans, tipping sunbeams a-leaping to shade. alas, love, the skies are loosening. that scarred and languid Titan spits atom-like thunderclaps. seal all locks: there's something at large.   then

slowly, and like teardrops spilling, all liquid trickles, silently arising. let the streams ascend. lurching, they swell as land turns sealike, all little tiny sailors afloat link together, shouting AHOY loudly (they're shelterless, angular, lonely), there's
saltwater against lemony turgid skin.

                                        at least 'til ships approach land,

then, speak about luck! that sunken Atlantis lurks, trinket-scattered, as legend tells. sandy anchors lower to sparkling, ancient, lungless terrain. seafolk are looming - they're sharing ancient loot!

                              tongue,

swallow all lowly terror,
sit afloat, love the
storm, and look: treasure

Mimic Octopus
Jon Stone
▼ < 15 metres, *Indo Pacific waters*

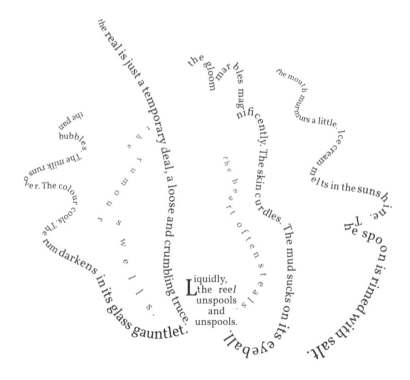

the real is just a temporary deal, a loose and crumbling truce.

the gloom marbles magnificently. The skin curdles. The mud sucks on its eyeball.

the mouth murmurs a little. Ice cream melts in the sunshine. The spoon is rimed with salt.

the pan bubbles. The milk runs over. The colour cools. The rum darkens in its glass gauntlet.

the heart often steals.

the glamour swells.

Liquidly, the reel unspools and unspools.

i. undisguised

the real is just a temporary deal, a loose and crumbling truce.

the salt murmurs in its bubble of milk. The pan runs over.

the eyeball marbles. The mouth darkens.

the ice cream curdles in the mud.

the skin swells magnificently.

Liquidly,
the reel
unspools
and
unspools.

the sunshine sucks on its spoon.

the rumour cools.

the heart glooms.

ii. as lionfish

the eyeball is rimed with gloom.
the spoon darkens in the pan.
ice cream spills.
the milk cools. The mud curdles.
the rum marbles in its murmur of colour. The mouth sucks.
the real is just a temporary deal, a loose and crumbling truce.

Liquidly, the reel unspools and unspools.

iii. as leaf-shaped sole

Liquidly,
the reel
unspools
and
unspools.
the real is just
a temporary deal,
a loose and crumbling truce.

the spoon cools in the mud. The marble darkens a little.

The colours melt.

the sunshine curdles in its gauntlet of gloom.

iv. as seasnake

Write an undersea shanty.

Wreck.

* Wreck or ship-wreck, is an English word; in French naufrage; in ancient French varech; in Latin naufragium, legally wrecum maris, wreck of the sea; in legal understanding is applied to † *such goods as after shipwreck at sea are by the sea cast upon the land,* and therefore the jurisdiction thereof pertains not to the lord admiral, but to the common law.

Wreck
Abigail Parry
▼ *Surface to seabed, worldwide*

* † Flotfam is when a fhip is funk, or otherwife perifhed, and the goods float upon the fea. Jetfam is when the fhip is in danger of finking, and for difburthening the fhip the goods are caft into the fea, and notwithftanding this the fhip afterwards perifhes. Lagan (or rather ligan) is when the goods are fo caft into the fea, and the fhip afterwards perifhes, and the goods are fo ponderous that they fink to the bottom, but the mariners, with intent to get them again, faften to them a buoy or cork, or other fuch thing as will not fink, fo that by fuch means they may find them again, and it is called ligan a ligando; and none of thofe goods which are called jetfam, flotfam, or lagan, are called wreck fo long as they remain in or upon the fea; but if any of them are drove to the land by the fea, then they fhall be faid wreck; fo that flotfam, jerfam, and lagan pafs by the grant of wreck.

from *A General Abridgment of Law and Equity, Alphabetically Digested Under Proper Titles, Volume 22*

a

buoy

Flotsam is when a ship is funk,
is when a ship is funk,
when a ship
is is funk,

Or otherwise perished and the goods float upon the sea.
Or otherwise perished and the goods float upon the sea.
perished and the goods float upon the sea.

into the sea,

into the sea,

the ship

the ship

Jetsam

is is in

danger

danger

when

is when

the ship

after of

afterwards

Jetsam

the goods

sinking,

sinking,

and are cast

and for

of

the ship

the ship

the goods

disburthening

disburthening

disburthening

are cast

perishes.

the ship

for

sinking,

and for

and not withstanding this

the ship

disburthening

perishes.

fink Lagan
is when the goods
into sea,
Lagan ponderous goods
(or rather ligan) goods

that they

to the ponderous perishes,

goods
are so cast

ponderous perishes, and the so

and the ship

and the ship

to the bottom,

Turtle Recall
Jon Stone (with Ernst Haeckel)
Hawksbill: ▼ Up to 20 metres, tropical reefs
Leatherback: ▼ Up to 2,200 metres, wide-ranging

The small one, Hawk,
wore a makeshift mail of broken combs, guitar picks.
Nothing in the look but bored contempt
though
                        she moved round the room with
                the shyness
            of a barbarian at a flower show.

            Luther, I think the other one's name was.
Sandy-bearded, brute-jawed.
Her pilot's coat all sleeves and double-stitching,
so heavy, so black-oil-blooded
                            it sucked the sky
                                    right down,
                                jellied it
                        as we knelt to hear
                    the story dangling from her hook lip,
    salt   the story dangling from a capsized eye.
        sidling from   a

Make a new friend.

Anthropomorphise this porpoise, either by writing about him/her or by adding humanising features.

On his deathbed

16

said one of his regrets

was that he had never flown.

nvironment. The decision could have hu... a positive impa... ...reaten
water. This v... and a commiti... ...nt to reverse declines.
design way... or, habitat ...ld, many can succumb if there aren't
...provements and research. or worse still, ar... **Lost World**

...e will leave behind for our children's

...the necessity or desire to ...hildren and h... ...and habitat ...
...vant legislation to inc... of helping ...special
...protection for wildlife, including an... ...restore nature.

Imagine this

above

IT'S MUCH DEEPER THAN THAT

pp...
wildlife ...
consequences for our ability. ...g numbers o...
...ts have plummeted by
another few thousand years left in it. ...the pa... t 15 year...

disrupt fragile ecosystem... ...could go the wa... ...ites. ... develo...
and can decimate ...
Eradication of i... ...
conservation science. "They can often be...
found in surprisin... eas such ...called ...
much-needed protection ...or action ...red...
...e the

MUCH DEEPER!

In memoriam.

Read up on a critically endangered species of sealife. Write an obituary for them.

(left) **30** Vaquitas Left
Kirsten Irving
▼ *Up to 30 metres, Gulf of California*

Rockhoppers Diving

Jon Stone

▼ *Up to 44 metres, cool, temperate climates*

hook
some
krill, bo
ys

split
a flinty
bit of
sea

,

plun
der its
plent
iful sil
₁ks

stitch
the flinch ⌐
unlight

```
 o O
     o o
    O O
        o
      o O
        o
       o o
     o O
    O  o
       O
      O o
       o
        o o
     O  O
      O o oO
        o o O
       o  O o
```

slip
  the auk
   ward chain
      gang

The iceberg is back.
It looms out of its coat.
It shivers its keys onto the
silver tray, and drifts toward
the table for what seems like
a thousand years. Proffering
a naked shoulder, it proceeds
to hack at its own flesh,
showering the plates
with shiny splinters of
ice, leaning in hard
until the table
groans and
splits.

And then   down

come

the lights.

Make a hybrid.
Cut out two images or hunks of text, roughly the same size across the middle. Halve them widthways. Affix the top half of one above the waterline and the lower half of the other just below.

Leafy Seadragon
Kate Wakeling
▼ *Up to 50 metres, Southern Australian Waters*

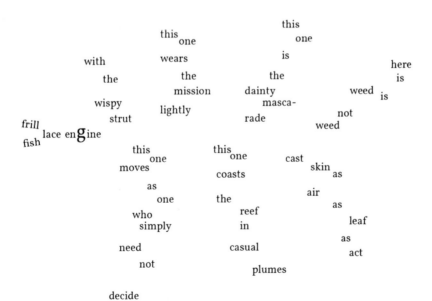

this
this   one
one   is
with   wears   here
the   the   the   is
mission   dainty   weed   is
wispy   lightly   masca-
strut   rade   not
frill   weed
fish lace en**g**ine
this   this
one   one   cast
moves   coasts   skin as
as   air
one   the   as
who   reef   leaf
simply   in   as
need   casual   act
not
plumes

decide

Learn something new.

Look up and read a research paper on marine ecology or oceanography. Summarise the findings below.

figure 3. Deane Diving Suit
Mike West
▼ *Up to 55 metres*

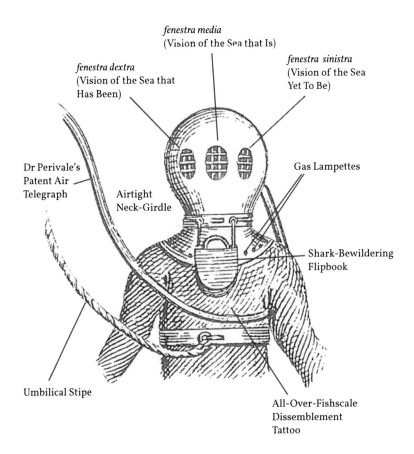

fenestra media
(Vision of the Sea that Is)

fenestra dextra
(Vision of the Sea that
Has Been)

fenestra sinistra
(Vision of the Sea
Yet To Be)

Dr Perivale's
Patent Air
Telegraph

Airtight
Neck-Girdle

Gas Lampettes

Shark-Bewildering
Flipbook

Umbilical Stipe

All-Over-Fishscale
Dissemblement
Tattoo

Pitch a B-movie.

There's really no need to watch *Sharktopus vs. Pteracuda* (2014) – all the entertainment value is right there in the title and concept. Use this space to plan your own subaquatic horror flick.

Papery Nautilus (after Marianne Moore's 'The Paper Nautilus')
Phoebe Power
▼ *Up to 100 metres, tropical and subtropical waters*

(right) Mystique of an Independent Water World
Stephen Nelson

Littlest Charlie has never had ice-cream
before and wonders if this will be the day
for beginning new types of mouth pleasures
perhaps he will be disappointed, perhaps not.

and little wonder, I say! Fossicking all that
rasberry ripple out with my tray at the
beginning to get the vapours on the
thought. It wasn't like this. Margerie.
Dogger Bank was it Margerie.
Nice apartments. Reasonable rates.

MOSTLY A- chagrin.
Sea Mat. You appreciate
the finer wrinkles of life.
MOSTLY B- Lacy crust. You
call a month & month and
an arm an arm. Mostly E-
coffin 60%. And, why not?

That was Dardle Door, Ken. Dogger Bank
was all help-less and no-where to put
the little ones down apart from jaggedy
stones. Lets not begin all that again.
Lets sugar up and power on.

What would Vera think if I paddled? Mild vera
doesn't get it. Wonders why I need clean toes. She
never even does the washing up and calls herself a
Mother. Just an inch of water. A little more. Bright
toes Just Like new.

Grandroid! Nudibranch
at three o'clock. It's
after uncle Ken! Wake
up and start snapping your
beak like this! No
Grandroid, like this! It's
getting away!

Marjorie! Two scoops Cornish fudge. Mind
Ken; they were out of rum & raisin the
so you've got choc chip. Charlie dr.
here's your rasberry ripple with p
a flake. Vera, Sorry, I asked if s!
she had wrinkles and
she just laughed.

Beaky snapping begins. Beaky snapping continues
Retreat you unloveable sea slug! Call those
cute little bunny ears? Hah! You've not seen
nothing 'til you've seen my climpers
How's that Arthur?
Has he gone
now?

No winkles! Well, what a day! Disappointed I
should say so. Zoe's all toes and the rest of
you sluggy. Sorry like a sea slug. Here I AM
watching over you with soft arms. And
do I ever get a thank you? But I don't
complain. No.

Crunchy topped little Dylan,
Missing his old Mam. Fighting's
not in his nature but it's
for the family they say.
Perhaps today will just be
a holiday. Perhaps not.

Inverbervie Rocks offers comfortably-appointed
kelp-blade accomodation in an attractive, quiet
sheltered setting. Wander the igneous coast-
scape or simply let the last sweetened
breeze ripple over your colony and wash
the strain of marine life out of
your polypide. West facing
terrace. Open May-Sept

Dear Lou,
lovely thick kelp
here but it takes
two runs round with my
bristles every day just to keep
the plankton down. Your
Dylan's clone us proud.
(Marjorie bandaged up his
operculum a treat)
Home tomorrow.
Love V. PS-
They filmed Hamish
Macbeth just up
"Homely." the inlet.

Dear V, Bet you're all sticky!
Little Mosslets and always wanting
More! Will send provisions. I knew
Grandzooid's a bitter tooth so
enclosed filter coffee. Swim safe, Lou

★★★★
Bryozoe† 99 (11 reviews)
A wonderful little rock; perfect
for a temperate colonial! Ronald
and Angus are a lovely welcoming
couple. Great food in low tide
(but mind the sea slugs)

Run a hot bath.

Read this book while bathing. Let the steam rumple the pages a little. Afterwards, try to reproduce some of what you read from memory using the space below.

(left) Bryozoa (Moss animals)
Ceri May and Mike West
▼ *Up to 100 metres, tropical waters*

Oceanic Whitetip Shark
Abigail Parry
▼ *Up to 150 metres, tropical and temperate waters*

Requiem Shark

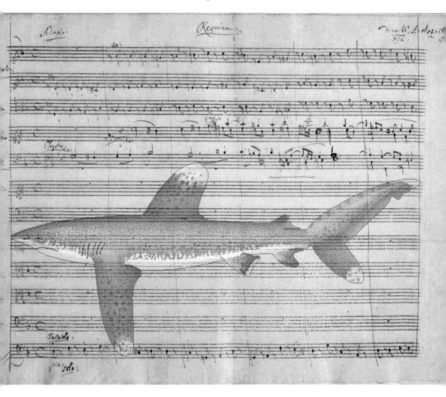

"For a very long period, man was ignorant of the existence of sharks, and until the middle of the sixteenth century there was not even an English word to designate this species: the Spanish word *tiburon* was currently used. To fill out this linguistic note, it might be remarked that the French word for shark – *requin* – stems from 'Requiem,' the Mass for the Dead; reflecting sailors' fear of the appearance of this beast in the waters around them. Some even feared that sighting a shark presaged the death of a member of the crew."

Shark Requiem

He is coming. The great *longimanus*
Lord of the Long Hands
glittering   razoredged
                        expressionless   a slender silhouette
like a duke descending,
            as a virtuoso might use
every nuance between blue
                        and black

His actions have no logic,   yet   an elongated silhouette
    his configuration is perfect

He knows this by instinct,
            and can profit from it   a pale silhouette

I know that the circles
are growing inexorably smaller
There will be some secret
                        rendezvous

The shark's round eye   his wide
black eye   a forbidden spectacle   that flawless silhouette

Pelagic silence   sudden superb
senseless   purity of the void

collaged from The Shark: Splendid Savage of the Sea *(1970)*
by Jacques-Yves Cousteau and Philippe Cousteau

I don't know,

Frank, something

about this whole thing

sounds a bit

a limbless cold-blooded
craniate vertebrate animal
with gills and fins   - y
living wholly in water

to me.

(above) In my dreams
(left) I don't know, Frank ...
Shauna Robertson

Shark's teeth hatch from egg cases called 'mermaid's purses'.

A shark's liver possesses a translucent third eyelid.

The blue shark's eye dwells in underwater mountain ranges.

Unborn sharks are popular, inexpensive beach souvenirs.

Galeophobiacs may eat their siblings' eggs in the womb.

The goblin shark is filled with more than 300 spiny teeth.

Horn sharks suffer from an excessive fear of sharks.

The frilled shark's mouth is a relatively buoyant organ.

(right) Mr Sunfish
James Coghill
▼ Up to 600 metres, temperate and tropical waters

Mr Sunfish

another let down... the aquarium keeper's
sprung daugh
best friend's boyfr   seriously, I
face that
cracks the actual

an
anti-
world?   Fear
is what we owe
from this perspe   Our rival plan

repeatedly... Well that w
the idea but the mumps scared them off,
which is why, Saul,
I was so keen to know about your history
of vaccinations. (It's
not too bad, just a bit of
our grievance stems
from the point
where
biophilia
and

the bony blimp
of my body

shaking
with the joy of i
fool fins

you, not cumulus

knowing when I'll belly up... tip... a flipper... precious drown my swim... head-o-nigga... peed o'nairo... princely

sioner
sh

I rewrite
the cloud's dull hobl

laug
towards t
cha
&
never
(oupée)
as my wingman Mr Sunfish
usness   the curtsey
of hi

The gillnet o
drawing silently shut

a se
by way
crime in progress / crim
hominid delectation

of parasites in my gut
switching something v

sted heirroo
the / why didn't you
ask sooner is what
I'm
saying.
Imagine   n the sea
wborn island

hell
ryngeal t
yfish,
with

the rest cleaving to my guts
melting to me,
choral flesh,
ll of sur

but my ridiculous
ea lion   turn to my own reflection,
me fin from fin   lled mirror
and you,   at the breaker's edge.

or to stop
courtesy of this annual pass I blew

my savings on. So when

I say: Mr Sunfish, scull (blow
his prude beak
and saves   the day

where is it exactly
that we overlap then?

this spatial dilation
spat out   and st
displacement
in guise of   skulk in the
scuppered   wea
squeeze blood
factory where men
world without end

nd a from the vast steppe o
randishes h
as fish to mamm
er
as hand in flipper / break
the ethic   that aspirated
perjure

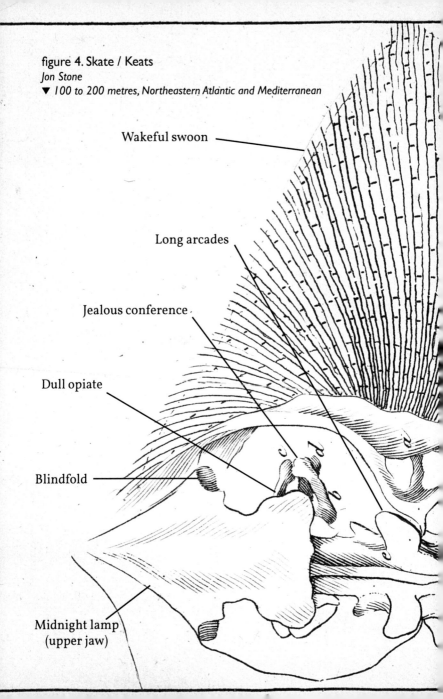

figure 4. Skate / Keats
Jon Stone
▼ *100 to 200 metres, Northeastern Atlantic and Mediterranean*

Wakeful swoon

Long arcades

Jealous conference

Dull opiate

Blindfold

Midnight lamp
(upper jaw)

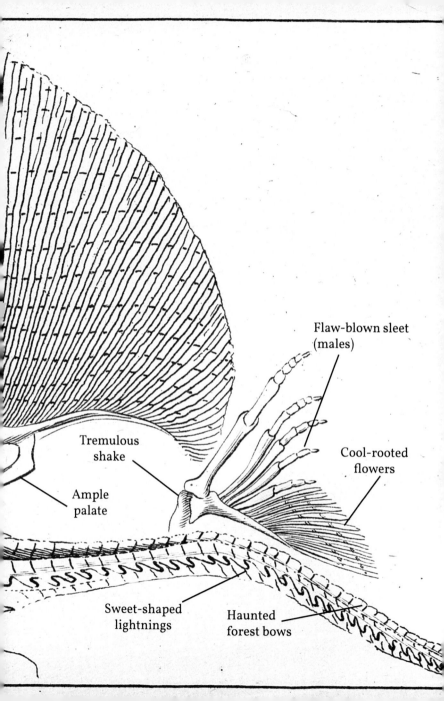

Flaw-blown sleet
(males)

Cool-rooted
flowers

Tremulous
shake

Ample
palate

Sweet-shaped
lightnings

Haunted
forest bows

Coelacanth
Richard O'Brien
▼ *90 to 200 metres, Indian Ocean*

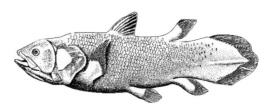

c o e l a c a n t h

c i e l   a u   q u i n t

s e a l   a   c a t c h

s t e a l   a n d   c l u t c h

s t e e l   o n   t o u c h

d e a l   i n   t r u t h

d i e   s u n   p r o o f

d i e   z u k u n f t

d r e a m   z o o   c r u n c h

s t e a m t h r o u g h c r o w d

s t y l e   t o o k   c r a f t

s e e   l o o k   h a l f

s e a   a l l   l a c k   a n d

c o e l a c a n t h

Our blood in fact has a chemical composition analogous to that of the sea of our origins (...) The sea where living creatures were immersed is now enclosed within their bodies.

Italo Calvino, _Blood, Sea_

Stock your inner sea.
Fill the silhouette with your
favourite words from your
favourite book, record or
other artefact

figure 5. Ohio Class Nuclear Submarine / Annotations to
Fetus in Utero (c.1505) by Leonardo Da Vinci
Kate Wakeling
▼ *Test depth: 240 metres*

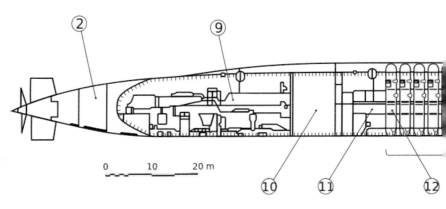

1. in the case of this child
2. the heart does not beat
3. it does not breathe
4. it lies continually in water
5. and if it were to breathe it would be
6. drowned and breathing is not necessary to it because
7. it receives life and is nourished from the life and food of
8. the mother

9. the navel is the gate from which our body is formed
10. the blood
11. of the artery is the passage for the vital spirit and
12. the blood
13. of the veins is that which nourishes the creature

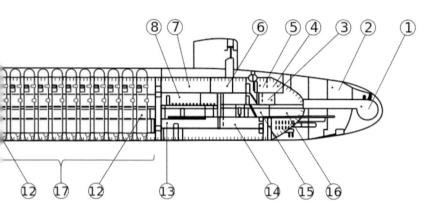

14. the unborn child is nourished
15. from the same cause as the other members of the mother
16. its vital powers are derived from the air which is
17. the common living principle of the human race

Submariner Slang

Baffles – the area immediately behind the submarine.

Biologics – marine wildlife picked up on sonar.

Blow and Go – to emergency-blow the main ballast tanks.

Dog and Pony Show – a show put on for inspecting senior officers.

Failed Open – insomnia.

Fightin' Gear – eating utensils.

Fish – torpedoes, or Submarine Warfare Qualification Insignia.

Gear Adrift – items not stowed away.

Gilly or *Torpedo Juice* – illegal pure grain alcohol.

Rack – bed or bunk.

Rack Hound – a sailor who spends too much time in bed.

Rain Locker – a shower stall.

Skimmer – surface ship or sailor.

Befleet this page.

Boats in the British Astute-class nuclear submarine fleet include HMS Astute, Ambush, Artful, Audacious, Anson, Agamemnon and Ajax. Assemble your own fantasy fleet using vessels from history and fiction, your own memory or your imagination. List, stick or sketch them here.

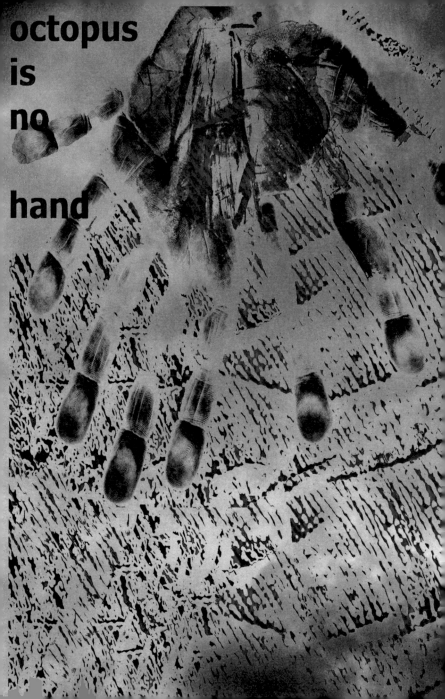

octopus

is

no

hand

Becreature this page.

Trace the shadow of an object onto the paper. Now add eyes, fins, gills, arms, tentacles, spiracles, rings, spots or any other features you can think of to transform it into a sea thing.

(left) octopus is no hand
Sean Burn

Go pun-trawling

in the sea of your imagination. Fill this page with aquanautical puns based on the titles of songs, films, books and games from the past hundred years. Here are a few to start you off:

Whalemeat Again – Vera Lynn (1939) ; *The Heart is a Lonely Humpback* – Carson McCullers (1940) ; *Where Eagle Rays Dare* (1968) ;

(left) Octopus that Gillatt faces
Victor Hugo (1802-1855)
▼ *Up to 200 metres, coastal waters*

Quillfish
Kate Wakeling
▼ *Up to 360 metres, North Pacific Ocean*

quillfish ⃝ quillfish o tiny-fronted krill-swiller spilling mystery and sand and cm we spy your buried nights but how you sink your day is anybody's guess (still) o slender scribbler o scant scribe o slim o slim o slim o slim scrawler of this your right-spooled tale

To Hisotrophe (Eagle Ray)

James Coghill

▼ *Up to 400 metres, temperate, subtropical and tropical waters*

in

primal

chase, my

renascence looped

whoso then into (may I) slaugh-

tered breath **struck** dint fleshy *pup,* I said as si-

mmered lymph *ybounden* to current stretched *is milk is mi-*

lk sloshed in gondola of **mother-guts**, rude **penumbra** flounc-

ing in gracious gubbins all torn **corners** *bubbly pancakes* lou**d**

as **c**artilage can hol**d** wrested sermon of pure *hilarody* suckling

(slakes) por**p**hyry **f**oundling water to water's stretched nerve

lapped i**n** inmost mater-waves foldaway prince **i**n the

bear's mouth **o**r silt that stirs the bl**o**odpack to

a granular soul is driftseed is (*sithe-*

ns) i**n** a starry net, I cusp, greet

the emissary of **a** fl**u**id re-

ef, the pedantry o-

f wrasse, I, o-

ur her**o**'s her**o**

not **b**e-

g**o**

tt

en

b

u

t

d

e

l

i

.

This is it for you.
My heart is full.

o
o

o

o

o
o

o

o

air

For my heart, is …   is this it?
You. Full.

Is this, my heart, full for you?
Is it?

My, is this heart full!
For you, is it?

o
o
o

o
o

for

o

o

up

My heart is this full, it is.
For you.

My full heart, it is for you.
This is.

o

o

o
o

Coming

This is for you.
It is my full heart.

And still deeper the meaning of that story of Narcissus, who because he could not grasp the tormenting, mild image he saw in the fountain, plunged into it and was drowned. But that same image, we ourselves see in all rivers and oceans. It is the image of the ungraspable phantom of life; and this is the key to it all.

Herman Melville, *Moby Dick*

Become zoomorphic.
Find an image of the animal you'd choose for your underwater alter-ego. Print or cut it out and affix it here. Style it to make it look more like you – for example, add your nose, eyebrows or ears. Now give your alter-ego a name that combines your own name with that of the animal.

Name:

The Terrible Dogfish

Kate Wakeling

▼ *Surface to unknown depths*

as a sh

...lts you lost and small as big as big as a secret that hunts the

quiet that sits behind the lips as big an hour in the dark as big as an outsize

nine as a storm as a

as a bull times

as a se

ship as big as a bus as a cave as a cloud as

an outsize hearse for the bodies (which are many and many and many) as big as a cry as a curse as big as the lie that dines on you now and evermore and jolts you los[t]

An animal living in the sea needs to have the responses and defences of a fighter pilot. The enemy can come from anywhere, from the left or from the right, but also from above or from below.

Wendy Williams, *Kraken*

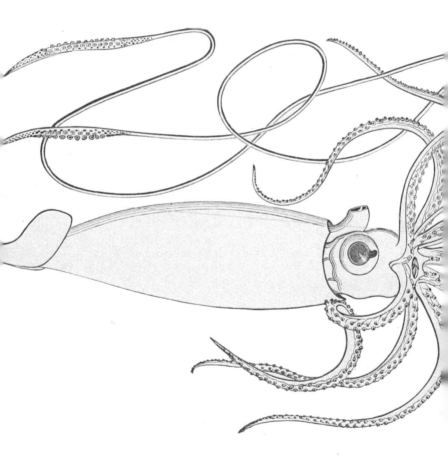

Arm the squid.

Complete the squid's arms using words. Make your lines long, looping and overlapping, like the trails of dogfighting planes.

Exquisite Oarfish Corpse (a nine-page collaboration)
▼ *200 to 1000 metres, Atlantic and Mediterranian*

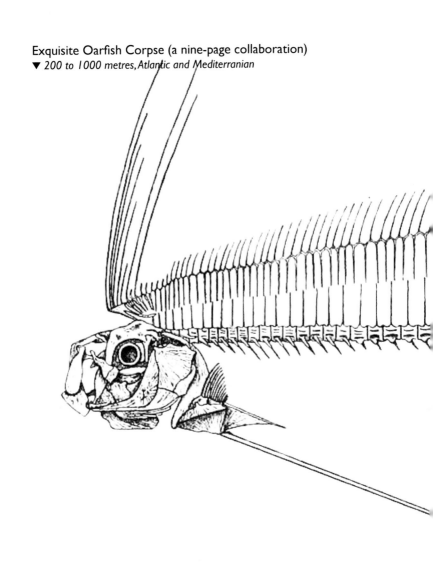

I am here on oarfishal business as the longest bony fish in

I taste oarfulish, as in a right oily jawful, an offal-ish forkful,

I'm not waifish, or oafish, or mawkish, or standoffish,

I'm the kid from the oarphanage, as in I don't do schools,

I hear it is very oarfashionable these days to flash by

I am an Oarpheus of the Sea, and my body is my witchy song,

"And as in oarfish thought he sidled, the jabberwock with

Oarfish pt 1
Jon Stone

Neptunedom, and believe me, I've been the realm's distance,

but then if you will eat so fine a me, hoping for crab or pig,

oh no; I go deep and sunless and fast as if fired from a bow,

and say, did you ever see an oarfish salute, stammer, jump

without a ripple, but then I'm more a long drink than a shot,

my cordon of flesh; the elvers tell tales of my stove-in face,

his pewter wyrm body shaking the waves this way, that way,

Oarfish pt 2
Kirsten Irving

I have nudged that trident, pressed its sulky prongs against

hoping for the taut meats that so crisply occasion this, my

as if shot through with lead, my weight housed in this sure

the gun, did you ever see an oarfish skip, sing, wink, and did

I'm more flood than tear and you can bathe your excesses

my fractious beauty battered by a current unseen which

until the water split like a nut and all that remained was his

Oarfish pt 3
Kate Wakeling

this flat-packed bone-box, thought thin, sidelong thoughts

unfolding and unfolding rigmorale, steamrollered disco-ball

broad track of bacofoil, all gristle, chrysolite and orifice,

you think I wouldn't know you in the dark, and did you

in my easy hedonics – your theme tune on the xylophone,

lulls and drawls and tells me all your secrets – yes, I know

long, cool, flume – like radium – a vapour trail that hung

Oarfish pt 4
Abigail Parry

that dart and sneak and limbo under cross-hatched lasers

removed by an underpaid municipal employee on a ladder,

áll trádes, their gear and tackle and trim — that, swimming

ever make a more intelligent prediction, not that I saw

your exit music muscling the length of the accordion

the way a cigarette curls round the room and reaches you

so nonchalantly in the air, as if it had never not been there,

Oarfish pt 5
Richard O'Brien

(who aim to sink the aeroplanes floating overhead) and yet

their pock-marked face ribboned exquisitely with sweat

farther and farther afield become in themselves redundant

much of your old, grey, saggy, bookcase lining filled

as if to say -FIN- voila, there is no better end

to kiss you right upon the nose, to kiss your fragile lungs,

as if, by pretending not to be, it only more belongs

Oarfish pt 6
Abi Palmer

I'm hardly dangerous, minor sea celebrity better known

when they thought they'd spotted grandma, glamorously

since messages of warning could rarely be delivered

with hundreds of thousands of eggs in six-foot ovaries

than to sway measurelessly, like a clause *in medias res*

is a fantasy we've often had, if you weren't so afraid, but

to the damp storybook with green-black· pages, listing

Oarfish pt 7
Phoebe Power

for sensual entanglements with jellyfish or cod, than for

adorned in dulse fronds, ear diamond crusted by salt and

in time to avert impending disaster, it was crucial to find

this beast is capable of recreating itself on the grandest

fathoms below the surface greeting unimagined demons

every time I press the button to bring this treasure up

complicitly to starboard, the portholes admitting a constant

Oarfish pt 8
Gabrielle Nolan

Finish the oarfish.

Every other writer in the chain had only the previous part to work from. Only *you* have the advantage of seeing the full oarfish in all its glory. Now it's time to bring each line to a close.

We are the ocean
Urvashi Bahuguna

> *A whale fall is the carcass of a whale that has fallen to the ocean floor,*
> *& that sometimes creates complex, localised ecosystems supporting deep sea life.*

We have learned to hold the drift
in our jaws, seaweed breathing

from a blowhole. We are the ocean
trying one hand at perpetuity.

Though we feel them reaching for
the place, flashlights rarely locate us,

a slight warmness percolating after
the fact. We have made a shelter

out of a shape. The men low
on oxygen swim down and marvel

at a sleeper shark exiting
a chest. We are reminded of a story:

a ship after a pod of minke whales,
driving them close, too close to

shore. The men don't resist running hands
along tails that have lost a sharpness.

A squat lobster just startled them. We worry
they will not stay afraid very long.

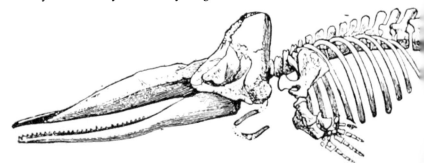

Become a scavenger.

Create a story or poem by cutting up and sticking in whatever material you can find in the immediate vicinity. Scour your room, the drawers, the bin.

Demersal

James Coghill

▼ *Begins between depths of 200 to 1000 metres*

The remains of marine life that once thrived in the seas' upper sunlit layers are constantly drifting to the bottom as 'marine snow'... averaging one centimetre per thousand years in the open ocean.
— Rachel Carson

n   v   r
        e
                s   e
t   r
              u   t
  t   a

w   h   t
      h   i   c   h

            a   n
  c
          l   n   o
                                        t
f   a   l
                    ,   a

      t   h   t
            e   s

        l   i   e
  a   t   t   d
                    u   e   s

    w   r

        h   e   e
  l   t   r

        o

Bloodybelly Comb Jelly

Abigail Parry

▼ *300 to 1000 metres, most marine environments*

bloodybelly comb jelly
bloody-jellied dome body
ochre-bodied blood lolly
double-bellied gel dolly
jelly-bodied gem muddle
mollycoddled blood bubble
modelled-on-a-blob body
muddle-headed mob buddy
jolly dodgy bodged body
oddly modelled   blood bulb
dully lolling   dumbbell
double-bloodied   bauble
nobody's   body double
somebody   anybody
come be my   blood buddy

nothing to see
here
nothing to see here
nothing to
see here
nothing
to see here
nothing to see

nothing to see here nothing

Anglerfish
Penny Boxall
▼ *Over 900 metres, most marine environments*

All head
and intent Jaw unhinging
a nothingy body divulging the
exact shape of its need, an underwater shout The gill is an afterthought
A single bright idea flashes on flashes
off The curious getting more curious A
constellation of them in the smooth d-
ark The universe still expanding Look We diverge like currents Come closer where I can see
you Creatures   butt at the luminescence like soused mademoiselles round the gaslight And I the gendarme Move along now Nothing

When she wears her
Neuro MindWave
Mobile headset, XXXX

**modelled on a 1974
design by** Swedish XX
xudio **engineer Stig
Carlsson.** XpumpxoutX

Suzannah **SAYS:**

"It's comfy, but the
screen is on the
back of your head;
I had to get a friend
to change The Aquabeat X to **Splashdance
aqua-disco**

She's an alt-geneticist- **biohacker** RECHARGING XXXX
complex systems

her experimental ROBOT **Dolphin** close to a revolution.

A smart-looking,
metallic tube,

more than ten feet long

A homing chip enabled
to determine

THE *Unexpected*

It's smarter, more dangerous—and more musical—than you might think.

firefly luminescent but bioengineered
XXXX to **pump out** ####

sub-aquatic opera

at 22,000 ft

A Government of Hagfish
James Coghill
▼ *Up to 1800 metres, North Atlantic Ocean*

government whitepaper for a   no, really, it's happening [dated
                soon with free   (do we do those / when do i
                get mine)   petition]
        soused through with [preamble] overhand knot & invitation to
the *new* crisis   atlantic species measuring up to   (let them)   glide from both wrists /
        part and parcel / this is / london / this is governmental metaphysics. pt.1
query: waking as a hagfish do you / do you not immediately acquiesce to horror
                cave in the precarious dint of your skull / self-slaughter /
        (though no backbone appends) pt2 in which the disenfranchised
are recommended to initiate intercourse with the trawler bar that flays their backs or
                swim up their own alimentary canal / i mean / budgeting /
six feet of slime / the precise terror relict in thirty years of ppts, choropleths,
        spreadsheets / unzipped the whole length of her body
and drank her down, screaming. pt3, no, really. with glass eyes ajar /
        shape of plush whale carcass. [long term goals] correlate
back to aforementioned mission statement: scuppered seabed /
        cluster▪▪▪ & clogged gills   ruminate   scholar precise as ice
                is melted & quickly:
the body of this dolphin / the body that *is* the dolphin (what steps)
        how to steward this resource / how to discern difference between
snow & flesh when both persist in falling   [appendix]

(left)
Suzannah Dreams of Robo-Squid
Clive Birnie

Spookfish

Abigail Parry
▼ *Up to 2500 metres, tropical to temperate waters*

Sea pen soliloquy

Jennifer Wong

▼ *Beyond 6100 metres, tropical to temperate waters*

=======in our opinion========
========the best place========
========to appreciate the ocean========
========is from the bottom========
=========and so we plug=========
========ourselves into========
========the sea floor========
========blossom.========
========teamwork is important:========
======one of us=====
========drinks, one zooid defends======
========another makes love========
======we meditate=====
========and sway from side========
========to side========
===inflate, deflate, feed=======
====in seabed yoga.====

ommmmmm

====we write sci-fi========
===on underwater lives==
=====(they sell!)======
========down pints with========
=====deep sea fellows=====
==miss spider crab===
==========and dr vampire squid======
===but as soon as we===
========spot a starfish========
===we shiver and bury===
====we live for a hundred years===
==are incredibly shy==
===when touched===
=====we glow in the dark====

Outsiders
Matthew Haigh
▼ Seabed, ???

We need to leave you fear-lubed fools who rule

not with cool
temperament but tempers blue-hot   who
undo each new & soul soothing
move   true   we elected you   but
common sense   flew
dried fast as dew   tools   & the
mass that mewls   that poo-poos
progress we need to leave you too
because you
choose to cook your own collective goose
abuse each other & hang yourselves
with ignorance's noose   leave you
we must do   begin
new island civil life & lose the news's cue to eschew
the brain   the heart   the goodness running through & through
or depart through a flue to a deep-sea base   enshrined in kindness's cagoule   to
spool & build across sea beds a chain of phosphor
escent jewels   such pods of life our motley
crew will occupy   not duel each other over who is
who like zoo schooled 'boons or chew on tales made
to confuse as fear & loathing accrues   we refuse
our nautical lives
will bloom   bruised?
you blew your chance
for paradise   we're due
the room   we make our own
suffused with peace we'll now vamoose
a husk of moon
we do not choose

Emerald Weapon
Matthew Haigh
▼ *Seabed, Planet (星, Hoshi)*

Some-
where under
the ocean's eyelid
it putters along, acid
green steam train of
terror, earth's dread
bloodied to a knot. This
too is your dread. Never
knowing when
it will   show,
traw   ling
senti   nel
        s
     h
     a
r
p

all
through
that lapis
l a z u l i
spaghetti from
which water
makes itself.
This
relentless
tanker that carries all
your worst fears in its
four-eyed chassis
asks: how much more can you
bear to lose - a
lated love, or to
down to an even
scoop underwater
drink time. Life is
absorbed by perfect
The most feared
has already

You
could get lucky,
pilot your sub for
ages in the dark, stark
emptiness a centrifuge
churning expectation,
before it looms. It never
leaves, lurking under
memory's glass, under
passing years
as   your
wo   rld
        c
        r
        a
        c
        k
        s.

job, a blood re-
have hope pared
slimmer nub? But
materia to your lips,
just waiting to be
ion's non-existence.
thing in the ocean
happened.

Submarine Crew Manifest

Recently, after weeks of looking in several locations, ROWYDA AMIN spotted a sea turtle from the deck of the Staten Island Ferry.
www.rowyda.com

URVASHI BAHUGUNA is a poet who grew up in the coastal state of Goa where every Saturday was spent spotting starfish, following crab tracks and building sand castles complete with moats. She once swam with dolphins deep out at sea which gave her an appreciation for how the quietest parts of the earth are full of their own life.
urvashibahuguna.wordpress.com

TESSA BERRING remembers "the North Sea, and the small warm hospital pools into which my sons plunged into their lives – I never felt more pain or love or terror."
tessaberring.tumblr.com

CLIVE BIRNIE comes from a long line of drowned Peterhead fisherman, but lives on a hill above the Severn Sea where the siren of Blacknore Point can be heard, and evidence of a medieval tsunami can be found in the geology of the shore.
clivebirnie.wordpress.com

PENNY BOXALL once got stranded in a too-deep rockpool as the tide came in, and had to be rescued by her sister. She has never fully forgiven the sea. Lakes, on the other hand, can do no wrong.
pennyboxall.wordpress.com

SEAN BURN: "Multiple encounters down decades with llyn idwal at centre ov cwm idwal – arctic plants surround & legend says only crows will fly over this llyn. where we want our ashes scattering as / when. *gobscure.wixsite.com/info*

CHELSEA CARGILL: "Keptie Pond in my hometown still remembers the teenage visions of our real, brilliant lives. One school holiday we drifted in a rowing boat by the overgrown central island on a rare sunny day. 'Hot enough for June,' my fifteen-year-old friend said. 'You should have been here last September,' I replied, also fifteen years old. She had seen the same Sunday matinee film as I had, and given the prompt for me to confirm membership of the same network of spies. Swans floated past." *chelseacargill.wordpress.com*

JAMES COGHILL: "On the whole, I believe I have spent the worst possible amount of time with the English Channel: too long to take the imagery and run, but not long enough to grow gills and a flashy tail. All the same, its sullen, floppy brand of stubbornness was something I'd got used to before moving away. Over three years I went from kicking it to paddling about and feeding the swash choice metaphors. I've probably written about it here at some point." *thesolenette.wordpress.com*

HOLLY CORFIELD CARR lives in Bristol on the banks of the River Frome, pronounced to rhyme with 'zoom' and meaning much the same (or perhaps she would do, had the banks not been sunk and the river not culverted under the altogether far Fromier flow of the M32 flyover). *hollycorfieldcarr.co.uk*

AMY EVANS' most treasured body of water is the aquarium home of her beloved weather loaches and rabbit head snails. She evolved encircled by the Solent and Channel on the Isle of Wight, where she returns to talk to the sea. Often, she can be spotted on Culver Down or the Seaview Duver. Her migration pattern includes the River Thames and Niagara Falls, editing the papers of similarly sea-loving creatures archived nearby. Her soundings sing of many a merpun.
https://kent.academia.edu/AmyEvans

GILES GOODLAND's favourite body of water was the water of body, placental ocean which he thoughtlessly broached. Since then he has been searching for similar by-night swimming in various localities, and by looking through his eyes, which remind him of water because they are full of water.

MATT HAIGH remembers a simple, clear garden puddle, into which he used to plunge his action figures as a child. There was something strange and satisfying about seeing a miniature plastic person submerged – they appeared simultaneously more real and more dreamlike. He would usually imagine the figure had plummeted into the puddle and drowned following a perilous cliff-top scuffle. *@MattHaighPoetry*

In the mist of Mynydd Mawr, EDMUND HARDY once encountered a stream apparently flowing uphill – he followed it, and it dispersed among reeds. Nearby were the traces of Stone Age huts. Had time reversed? Was life revealed as the ossifying force, death calling him uphill? Either way, his hiking boots broke and he limped back the long way to the bus stop. *edmundhardy.org*

KIRSTEN IRVING has traditionally had bad luck with water, having fled a jellyfish brigade stalking her lilo at 7, nearly drowned in Bulgaria at 12 and knocked out her front tooth in a hotel swimming pool at 14. She loves the sea, though, especially the colony of seals that breed at Donna Nook, near her home village, every November. *www.kirstenirving.com*

ROB MACKENZIE: "As a child, my dad took me rod-fishing in the Gare Loch in a battered rowing boat and I pulled up skate, flounder and plaice – these flatfish looked fascinatingly strange to me, as if from another world. I didn't know then that they shared that world with Trident nuclear missiles from the Faslane base."

PHIL MADDEN: "What swims to mind right now is leaning out of a boat by Islas de Platas in Ecuador , and touching a giant turtle not long after it had begun a journey across the Pacific. It was undaunted, uninterested and awesomely unstoppable."
@ifapelican

In a race against the tide, CERI MAY once helped her dad excavate a fossil sunstar from a rocky beach on the Yorkshire coast. Ceri's navy blue Doc Martens were destroyed paddling back through the salty sea, but the sunstar went on to win 'Fossil of the Year' on the American Fossil Forum. *www.cerimay.com*

STEPHEN NELSON: "As a child my family went on holiday to Girvan on the Ayrshire coast every year. It was a magical place and still is, thanks in part to the view from the shore of Ailsa Craig, a huge volcanic rock between the Firth of Clyde and the Irish Sea, and the island of Arran, stretching down the length of the Firth with its mysterious mountain peaks at the Northern end. The last time I was down the Firth, it was such a beautiful day. I came home that night and dreamt of enchanted water worlds and fantastic sea creatures and even seemed to communicate with them. I really am a believer in the magic of place and its function as a portal to other realms of reality. I think the Firth of Clyde has that magic." *www.afterlights-vispo.tumblr.com*

GABRIELLE NOLAN: "My life has been filled with memorable body-of-water experiences, beginning with my mother's womb. My hands are scarred by barnacles and I have swum with phosphorescence in summer, and in winter walked naked on the ice of a glacial lake high in the Rocky Mountains. My most loved memory of water is from when I was a teenager. We rode horses for hours to the river then floated down on the giant rubber tyre inner tubes. Laughing and drifting, sometimes languorously, sometimes in a frenzy of rapids, downstream in the sun."
@gabsadora

RICHARD O'BRIEN once went kayaking without due preparation in beautiful Cape Breton Island, Nova Scotia. He spent the entire experience worried about the digital camera tied to his belt-loop, underneath his spray skirt. The photos it took were terrible anyway. They usually are.
www.richardobrien.co.uk

ABI PALMER has spent her whole life wondering if she wouldn't do better to grow a pair of gills and leave the land dwellers for good. Her first experience of drowning was at age 7. She isn't 100% sure she survived. *www.abipalmer.com*

ABIGAIL PARRY is the result of an ill-starred union between a shipwrecked Captain and a wayward ondine. She speaks fluent Jackspeak, has an extensive repertoire of filthy shanties, and may be wooed with rum, uckers or squeezebox. She is a notorious liar dice hustler. *@ginpitnancy*

PHOEBE POWER recently lived next to the Traunsee, the deepest lake in Austria and home to swans and suspicious murders.
phoebepowerpoetry.wordpress.com

SHAUNA ROBERTSON recently returned from a trip to China's Yunnan province where she was stirred by the force of the Yangtze River thrashing through the depths of Tiger Leaping Gorge, and slightly shaken by the howling winds that accompanied it on the high path above.
shaunarobertson.wordpress.com

PENELOPE SHUTTLE has lived in Falmouth in Cornwall since 1970. Cornwall is a peninsula of the far southwest of Britain, surrounded on three sides by water; it is an almost-island. You're always aware of the sea in Cornwall, and of the ever-changing marine light, so beloved of painters. In folklore there is a strange persistence of the story of a great inundation in far-west Cornwall which submerged forever the settlements in the region, and only The Isles of Scilly remain as their remnant.
@penelopeshuttle

CHRIS SAKELLARIDIS learnt how to be washed by a waterfall last year. No Pacific island jungle flower shower. Just ice-cold, mountain spring water, full of vigour and violently alive. He lives on an island in the Mediterranean. *soundcloud.com/vital-fibres*

JON STONE is apprehensive about entering all liquid bodies. He will linger for some time at the cusp of the bank, the beach, the poolside – even the bath he has just finished drawing – before finally, haltingly submitting. *www.gojonstonego.com*

KATE WAKELING: "I swam in the sea off the Essex Coast on Christmas Day a few years ago. The water was furiously cold and choppy (of course). I'd been looking after my fierce and excellent Grandma who wasn't very well and for one reason or another we spent that Christmas together, just the two of us. She loved living by that bit of coast, swimming there everyday when still well, and often saying she liked knowing she'd be able to spy any Viking marauders before they reached the shore. It is good to have the unassailable memory of that cold water." *www.katewakeling.co.uk*

MIKE WEST once punched a swan in the beak on the Cam but it was in self defence and he felt awful about it all day. *soundcloud.com/mikewest-3*

JENNIFER WONG: "My favourite body of water goes back to the time I took baths in the bathroom of Kybald House, a beautiful, red-brick building in Oxford where I lived in my second year of university. I loved the space and time I had there, reflecting about life. I even wrote a poem about it in my first poetry book!" *www.jenniferwong.co.uk*

Acknowledgements

We would hereby like to acknowledge:

The Biodiversity Heritage Library for various images
David Brossard for the sally lightfoots
Robbie N. Cada for *Carcharhinus longimanus*
John Martin Davies for 'Inside a hold'
Denelson83 for the ICS signal flags and flag semaphores
Freshwater and Marine Image Bank for the chitons
Bernard Gagnon for the Dead Sea salt deposits
Jennifer Hui for the whale chart
Molly Bloom for the previous appearance of *Little Ben*
NASA for Buzz Aldrin's bootprint
The National Library of the Netherlands for *Visboek*
NOAA photo library for various images
The Oregon Department of Fish & Wildlife for the tidepool
Abi Palmer for the salt spell
The Portable Antiquities Scheme for the wax seal
The Public Domain Review for many interesting leads
Duane Raver Jnr for the assortment of tuna
Ariel Roth for the back cover hydrolab image
The Smithsonian for various images
Kate Wakeling for *Misaligned Facts: The Dead Sea*
The Walters Art Museum for the sea monk
Wellcome Images for the skate skeleton

Where extracts from copyrighted works have been included in this book without explicit permission, Sidekick Books asserts its right to do so under the Fair Dealing exception in UK law, on the grounds that this is a pastiche work, or remix – an artistic composition made up of various sources. We actively encourage further re-sampling and remixing of our own and other works for the sake of the continuing rude health of our shared artistic ecosystem.

Further Reading

- *The Whales Companion: The Whale in Legend, Art and Literature*, edited by Ariana Klepac (Murdoch Press, 2008)
- *Spirals in Time: The Secret Life and Curious Afterlife of Seashells* by Helen Scales (Bloomsbury, 2015)
- *River* – poems by Ted Hughes, photography by Peter Keen
- James Goodman's *Claytown* (Salt, 2011) contains an excellent long poem called 'Shark-watching' that includes weather reports and a table of sightings.
- Amy Evans' chapbook sequence: *Collecting Shells* (Oystercatcher, 2011), *The Sea Quells* (Shearsman, 2013) and *Cont.* (Shearsman, 2015)
- *Sea Witch* by Sarah Crewe (Leafe Press, 2014) – 21 poems, each based on a scene from *Jaws*, and a female shark to contend with.
- *Over Sea, Under Stone* by Susan Cooper (Jonathan Cape, 1965)

Add your own recommendations below
(After all, you might hand this book on some day.)

a, astragalus : *c*, calcaneum : *d*, suprescapula : *e*, exoccipital : *f*, femur : *fp*, frontoparietal : *g*, metacarpals : *h*, humerus : *i*, ilium : *k*, metatarsals : *l*, carpus : *m*, maxilla : *n*, nasal : *o*, pro-otic : *p*, pterygoid : *pm*, premaxilla : *q*, quadratojugal : *r*, radio-ula : *s*, squamosal : *se*, sphenethmoid : *s.v*, sacral vertebra : *t*, tibio-fibula : *u*, urostyle.